To my friend Raven
with best wishes
& hope you enjoyed
your stay at CFA.
[signature] July 2017

STORY TELLING

FROM ME TO YOU

A compilation of short stories, yarns, rhymes and blogs.

SOME ARE LONG
AND SOME ARE TRUE
THERE ARE ONES
THAT ARE SHORT
AND OTHERS ARE BLUE
ALL ARE THOUGHT PROVOKING
WITH FUNNY ONES WORTH A
GIGGLE OR TWO

STORY TELLING

FROM ME TO YOU

ISBN 978 0 9956917 1 1

Published by

Percychatteybooks Publisher

As always for my lovely wife Jean, friend and soul mate, who has helped with the editing and all rewrites, also listening to all my ramblings whilst putting these articles together.

My appreciation to the following

Derek Cook for the cover

Christopher Wyatt

Richard Seal

Tony Brown

Pete Broadbent

All my friends on Social Media who send me their gems.

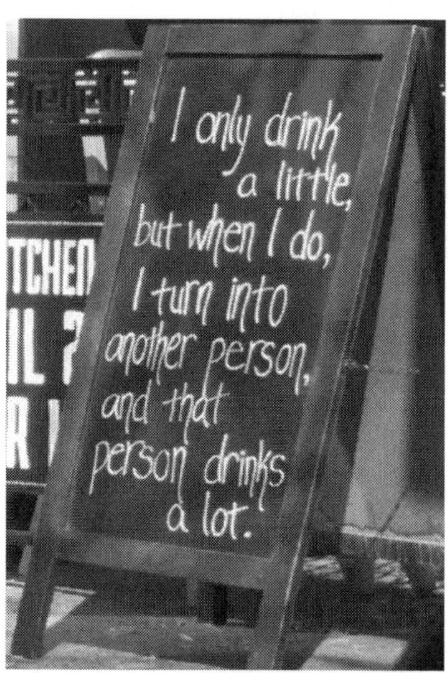

Contents

Guard Dog!! I would bet the vision that has come to mind is an Alsatian, a Doberman or something similar snarling and showing its teeth whilst straining at a chain daring an intruder to go near it. Let me introduce Meg, a darling little black and white lady about the size of a Jack Russell, our Guard Dog! I would not say she is lazy but she does things very differently, not for her snarling and running up and down – no she sits on the settee and studies the CCTV monitors, and if anyone comes in sight then she barks even before they have got to the door bell.

MEG

"Welcome to our book of short stories!" Let me introduce Meg our clever little furry lady friend who will help throughout this work to describe, where needed, the origin of certain stories.

'lol' arrived in the English Language via the texting requirement of keeping phrases short. It is recognised as meaning 'laugh out loud' but then again it could mean anything 'Love of London' for instance or Limerick. Sometimes it is a little confusing for example in the middle of a recent newspaper report there was the initials 'GMP' – it could be 'Good Morning Padre' or 'Grey Men Parading' it is possible to think of many alternatives, however as one continued to read the story it meant 'Greater Manchester Police.'

This reminds me of my Army Training when I was in the Royal Engineers as a Signals man in a Regiment. It was always made exceptionally clear to be certain what you are saying and cannot be misunderstood as something different to what is intended, their example of how a signal could be misread was 'The regiment is going to advance' be certain it cannot be interpreted as 'The regiment is going to a dance.'

'HAGRAPAGL' – have a great read and perhaps a good laugh.

The Chancer

From Percy's novel 'Time Gentlemen' this part of the novel may seem a bit strange and unbelievable but during the Second World War many civilians were killed and one in three properties destroyed. It follows that after the event there was not always a secure record of ownership.

In the early nineteen forties when the Second World War raged around Great Britain, with enemy bombers attacking in their swarms and causing mayhem to each of the cities. In a busy part of Guildford on the corner of a main road, stood a large furniture store, with a stunning eye-catching façade, called Donaldson's after the owner, who was a man in his sixties. He was a person, although a regular visitor to the church, who earlier in his youth had avoided family life. Richard, frequently shortened to Dick was an exceptional person in that he strived to keep his independence, and shunned company.

On the top floor of his store, which had been built in the Victorian period, around the eighteen thirties, was a large comfortably furnished flat. This is where he spent most of his time, when he was not attending to the needs of his business in the substantial show room on the ground floor, with its generous size of space.

It was Autumn and late evening, he was sitting at his desk, going through the figures in the accounts, when the first wailing of an air raid warning sounded. After months of the familiar noise warning of an attack which sometimes did not happen, he took little notice and continued with what he was doing. In the distance he could hear gun fire perpetrated by the ground forces trying to repel the attackers. As time went past and the raid continued, he looked up as he was aware the air incursion was coming closer to where he was sitting. There was the detonation of an exploding bomb close by, the flash from the discharge lighting up the window frame where the blackout curtain did not quite fit. He quickly left the room and retired to the spot under the stairs, which he had previously made comfortable for such an event.

Although he had heard the initial whistle of the bomb which penetrated the centre of the furniture store, hurtling through it and finally exploding in the basement, Richard knew nothing of it as it had demolished the stairway. The following blaze consumed the building and the fire officer, who was overwhelmed by the amount of destruction the bombers were creating that night, instructed his men to abandon Donaldson's to its fate and try to save other buildings which were not so badly damaged.

It was a few years after the war had come to an end, when the City Council took on the task of trying to link damaged properties, where the occupier was missing, to their rightful owner or relatives- However no matter how much they tried it was not possible to find a person who was related to Richard Donaldson. What was left of the unsupported structure of windowless brickwork standing as a memorial to its past glory, was deemed to be unsafe and was pulled down at the Councils expense, and the site levelled and cleared.

Harry Cox, whose father had been a car trader before the hostilities, with the strict restrictions on the use of cars at the start of the war, brought his activities in his endeavours to earn a living by this means, to an end, especially more so when the Army required his services in a foreign land from which he did not return.

Now, the War was over and the horrors of it were becoming a distant memory, his son was not one to miss an opportunity. Over a period of time he watched the area being cleared, and now the last of the council's plant was leaving the site and the final lorry of rubble was being taken away. He lost no time in getting in touch with a friend and between them they moved two of the cars from his father's old stock, which had been residing in a barn, since before the war. Cleaning them throughout so they sparkled and also trying to hide any rust, they moved them to the empty plot where they put a for sale sign on them. In the years after the war it was a period when there was a heavy demand for cars, as there were very few new ones being produced for the home market, trade was brisk.

Time drifted past and to Harry's surprise no one questioned the use he had put the valuable location to, and as his confidence grew he erected an office and finally a brick structure. He had one problem and that was the lack of energy to work the lights, and as he was not too certain of the tenure he had on the property, he did not want to go to the heavy cost of putting power lines in.

One morning he arrived to find the Local Authority was installing new street lighting. To achieve this they had dug deep trenches close to the boundary of the car plot to install the electric cables. Harry looked at the work and had an idea. After talking to another one of his buddies, who was in the know about electricity, they came to a decision. One Sunday afternoon when no Council work was being carried out on the lighting, a small gang of men made a connection to the new facility that was being installed, and ran a cable to the office of the car sales, disguising the work they had carried out so that it would not be seen. With some trepidation, Harry waited for the new street lighting to be activated, and when it was, to his total surprise, he pressed a switch and he had electricity.

And now fifteen years since selling his first car from the site, the place was a blaze of colour from its neon lighting declaring in giant red letters Harry's Car Lot and a row of shining cars, lined up on the front, with bright plastic stickers showing the price and other detail.

It was the week before the Easter break, and Harry watched as two people entered the site and was looking at one of the American cars, which he specialised in. He left them for a little while to see if they were really interested before, dressed in a smart grey tailored suit, he went out to speak to them. The punter was opening the door of the Chevrolet Impala and peering inside the gleaming vehicle. Harry was walking slowly to them wondering if they had a car to part exchange, and what make and year it would be. The clatter of the outside telephone bell shook him out of his thoughts. Returning to the office he picked up the instrument, and immediately recognised who the caller was.

"Hello Harry, we missed you at the game last weekend, and what do you know that bloody Calvin, whatever his other name is, kept winning the pot – would you believe it?"

"The trouble is Charlie, I do believe it, I can't help feeling, and I am sure others feel the same, he is cheating somehow."

"Well some of us want to take him to the cleaners and we are hoping you will be there to help – what do you say?"

"Look Charlie, I have a punter on that piece of junk of a Yank, which I have regretted ever having bought as I paid too much money for it, so I must go – is the game going to be at the usual place and time?"

"Yeah, seven thirty in the Casino at The Black Rose, I have been ringing round and I think we will have a full house, as all the team will be there, see you Saturday." Harry was putting the phone down when he heard the other speaking "We thought we would meet in the bar for a livener first"

"That is fine with me, now I must go as they are crawling over the car, I've got a feeling they are going to buy it."

"In that case the first round will be on you. See you Saturday."

Harry went back out to hopefully sell the vehicle. After taking the couple who were excited, in the car for a demonstration ride, they returned to the office where they parted with their money, and as the new owners drove away in their purchase.

**

'Most folks are about as happy as they make up their minds to be!'

Percy didn't write that Abraham Lincoln did!

Mountain path

A thousand ago and more
this mountain path was here
the rocks beneath our feet unmoved
as humans disappear.

These stunning views are stilled in time
eternal valleys deep
beneath dark trees sink into peace
of everlasting sleep.

As generations pass this way
to stand in shock and awe
at nature's wonders, mountains find
these people such a bore.

And deep within the chiselled crags
I sense a subtle mock -
This fool is glancing at his wrist
and thinking of the clock!

Email: richard@seal2244.fsnet.co.uk
Tel: (0034) 622 299 367

** *A Teachers Lament:*

The children are sitting in class for a religious lesson and the teacher asks them, "If I sold

my house and my Car, had a big jumble sale and gave all my Money to the church, would that get me into heaven?"

"NO!" the children answered.

"If I cleaned the church every day, mowed the garden and kept everything tidy, would that get me into heaven?"

Again, the answer was 'No!'

By now she was starting to smile. "Well, then, if I was kind to animals and gave sweets to all the children and loved my husband, would that get me into heaven?"

Again, they all answered 'No!'

She was just bursting with pride for them and continued, "Then how can I get into heaven?"

A six year old boy shouted, "Yuv got tae be dead"

**

My colleague and I were eating our lunch in our cafeteria, when we overheard an admin girl talking about the sunburn she got on her weekend drive to the beach. She drove down in a convertible, but said she 'didn't think she'd get sunburned because the car was moving'.

They Walk Among Us!

**

One day I was walking down the beach with

Some friends when someone shouted.....

'Look at that dead bird!'

Someone looked up at the sky and said...'where?'

They walk among us!

Somewhere in Paris

The forword from Percy's thrilling Novel 'A Common's Mistake'

Just prior to the large increase in oil prices in 1974, an influential Arab, who had the ability to soften the blow for the industrial nations, sat at the head of the table in the boardroom of one of his many companies. His patience was wearing thin as the monthly meeting stretched beyond its time limit.

Outside the heavy curtained window that overlooked a narrow Paris street leading to the Champs Elysees, the sun was vying with the clouds in an attempt to warm the city. At the end of the turning, seated beneath a coloured awning amongst numerous tables and chairs, Paulo looked at his watch and noted that their schedule was starting to run late.

He looked down the street. Half-way along his companion waited in a Transit van, which had been acquired for the occasion. The bonnet was open, on the pretence that it had broken down. Sue, a pretty and yet nondescript-looking girl, was patiently waiting behind the wheel. Passersby and traffic police glanced at the stricken vehicle and without further thought continued about their business.

Paulo looked at his watch once more and pondered on the wisdom of ordering a third cup of coffee. His prey was nearly an hour late from the timings of his normal monthly meeting, and the agreed time limit between the partners had expired. He continued to wait, years of experience guiding him. At his feet a duffel bag concealed an automatic small arms weapon loaded and cocked, waiting to spit out its deadly missiles at the hands of the master who temporarily possessed it.

Beyond the van, patiently waiting in front of a tall office block in a small slip road, stood a limousine. Its owner a few floors up looked at the wall clock, and with firmness, as he came to a decision he stood up, declaring the meeting closed, adding that the matter being discussed was wasting his time, and could be put on the agenda for the next monthly meeting. Immaculately dressed in a dark business suit, he left the room.

Had anybody been observing that meeting, they would have noticed that there was one who had been trying to hurry matters along, knowing that time was short if the plan that had been devised to destroy the powerful objection to their course was to take place. Hastily looking at his watch as the meeting broke up, he hoped that the paid assassins had waited longer than arranged.

The light grey Mercedes edged away from the building into the street and slowly made its way towards Paris's main thoroughfare less than two hundred metres from where it had waited. Nobody noticed that the bonnet of the van was closed and that the engine sprang into life as Sue regained the driving seat.

Discarding his third cup of coffee Paulo walked towards the junction with the famous street, his timing matching the pace of the big car.

The car and the gunman arrived at the junction at the same time. The Arab, busy studying papers in the rear, was not aware of his surroundings, only one of his two bodyguards taking any notice of Paulo, and then without any alarm. Sue pulled the van away from the kerb, following the larger car a short distance behind, the sliding side doors locked in the open position. The Mercedes stopped at the junction, and the driver looked in horror as the young person dropped the bag. In his hand the sterling sub machine gun looked black and ugly

The bodyguard, who had given the man but a cursory glance, suddenly realised the danger and loudly cursed his lack of alertness. He watched as the gun, which appeared to be moving in slow motion, swung round towards him. He swiftly went for his own revolver tucked in a holster under his arm, knowing that he would not make it.

His boss, sensing the danger, looked up, and as he did so he saw the flashes from the stubby barrel of the automatic as the weapon spat out its message. Pedestrians stopped and stared as the noise echoed around the busy streets and buildings. The windows of the car disintegrated, the blood sprayed its interior as the men died instantly. Only the chauffeur remained alive, severely wounded as he slumped over the wheel, setting the horn off in an incessant blast.

Paulo left the scene, knowing his mission was accomplished. Sprinting to the van that was gathering speed, he threw himself in through the open side door and disappeared, with Sue expertly steering the vehicle through the traffic. Minutes later, their disguises removed the van abandoned, the couple vanished.

From the novel 'A Common's Mistake'

**

Teacher to child in class
"How old is your father?
Child "He is six."
Teacher "How is that possible?"
"He didn't become a father until I was born."

Flush

Spider's legs wiggle
wriggle before body
in triumph emerges
from plug hole.
Escaped dark depths
to walls porcelain
sheer, footing faltering
on slip surfaces.
Lifted free by scoop
swift, swept from bath
to bowl and toilet
final flush.

Email: richard@seal2244.fsnet.co.uk
Tel: (0034) 622 299 367

**

I couldn't find my luggage at the airport baggage area and went to the lost luggage office and reported the loss.
The woman there smiled and told me not to worry because she was a trained professional and said I was in good hands. 'Now,' she asked me,'Has your plane arrived yet?'...
(I work with professionals like this.)
They Walk Among Us!

A thought provoking Poem by Tony Brown concerning the Great War, if only what he proposes could become true.

...to end all wars:

They called it The Great War
The war to end all wars
If only that were true
I'll give you a few statistics
Maybe some you already knew

Eight and half million soldiers killed
Nine million civilians too
Twenty million wounded
These just the ones we knew

A whole generation of young men and boys
Wiped out and discarded like broken toys
In one battle alone sixty thousand men slain
And that was just on the first day
Nearly two million shells were fired in vain
And that was just going to be the way

Life in trenches was beyond all belief
Two weeks at a stretch without any relief
Up to their ankles in deep mud and water
Then over the top to engage in the slaughter

But on one Christmas Day the guns ceased to chatter
They decided that one day of peace wouldn't matter

They came out of their holes to sing carols and chat
They played football, yes, football
How crazy was that
They gave gifts to each other as brother to brother
But the following day they were killing each other
Does this not inform us how futile is war
When men can kill men
They made friends with before
Simply because it is all one can do
If you don't kill the enemy he will kill you

If we would strife to justify the killing and the pain
It can only be by lessons learned to not go there again
The war to end all wars it was supposed to set us free
A very sobering thought indeed but it was not to be

Just twenty one years later it all begun again
And millions more from every side
gave up their lives in vain

Why should any race or creed be made to follow orders
To maim and kill their fellow man
And invade each other's borders

Another conflict, thousand dead
Woman and children in their beds
Beautiful cities left to burn...
When will we learn

Why can't we share resources

That are found upon this earth
Then everyone around the world
would be of greater worth
Why can't we lead our own lives,
not interfere with others
Maybe then and only then
there'll be far fewer
Grieving mothers.

Tony Brown August 2014

**

One of Percy's Blogs written December 2016

It is a great way to finish the year with a notification I have once more won my fifth NABE Award (National Association of Book Entrepreneur) this time for 'Time Gentlemen' in the 'Adult Fiction' Category. The novel is set in the 1970's and is a thrilling story of how a group of people, unknown to each other are involved in a terrifying event. The book is available through Amazon and all eBook outlets.

Sometimes one has to smile, if not laugh, while some experts go on about global temperatures' being on the rise and yet we have just had the coldest December in the sixteen plus years we have been in this beautiful part of Spain. We have vivid memories of our family visiting us in the last few or early months of the year and going back home with a tan, after lying in the sun by the pool. So I do not understand how the so called experts come to a conclusion it is getting warmer.

Yesterday I took our little mongrel dog down the campo to the rear of our villa. The almond trees are bare although the first buds are forming promising the valley to be covered in beautiful pink flowers. The sky was a perfect blue - a stunning sight in itself. I stopped for a while and there was not a sound – absolute silence. Somewhere down in the valley I could see a tractor, doing what tractors do going up and down a piece of ground, however the noise it was making did not carry to where I stood. It occurred to me that is what the totally detached property of Casa FuenteLargo represents, peace and quiet, a place to relax with nothing or no one to trouble our guests. No doubt that is why we have visitors, who lead a stressful life, coming back time after time to recharge their batteries and leave us once more to go home totally refreshed.

To complete the comfort of the Villa is the local village of Hondon de los Frailes nestling in the valley with its picturesque charm, small general stores and a variety of restaurants serving delightful food. For further information go into Facebook and look up 'Whats on Hondon.'

**

People who wonder whether the glass is half empty or half full miss the point. The glass is refillable.

Grandpa Story to Be Proud Of

Last week, I took my grandchildren to a restaurant. Before we ate, my 8-year-old grandson asked if he could say grace.

As we bowed our heads he said, "God is good, God is great. Thank you for the food, & I would thank you even more if Grandpa gets us ice cream for dessert - and liberty & justice for all. Amen!"

There was laughter from the other customers nearby, except one woman who I heard remark, "That's what's wrong with this country? Kids today don't even know how to pray. Asking God for ice cream! Why I never!" Hearing this, my grandson burst into tears & asked me, "Did I do it wrong Grandpa? Is God mad at me?" After I assured him that he had done a terrific job & that God was certainly not mad at him, an elderly gentleman approached the table. He winked at my grandson & said, "I happen to know that God thought that was a great prayer." "Really?" my grandson asked. "Cross my heart," the man replied. Then, in a theatrical whisper, he added (indicating the woman whose remark had started this whole thing), "Too bad she never asks God for ice cream. A little ice cream is sometimes good for the soul."Naturally, I bought my grandchildren ice cream at the end of the meal. My grandson stared at his ice cream for a moment, & then he did something I will remember the rest of my life.

He picked up his sundae &, without a word, walked over & placed it in front of the woman. With a big smile he told her, "Here, this is for you, you grumpy old bitch. I hope you enjoy it!"

Climbdown

Her hot feelings ran so hard
and fast, red raw emotions,
searing and sore, escalated
rapidly around narrowed eyes
flashing, tongue lashing, words
slashing, flesh scarlet flushing ..

Calming slowly, gasp-grasping,
left teetering now over precipice
of high dudgeon. Knows painful
climb-down required, but too fired;
contrition be damned, this door
is begging to be slammed.

Email: richard@seal2244.fsnet.co.uk
Tel: (0034) 622 299 367

The Swarm:

By Christopher Wyatt

The setting: A house in Spain on a mountainside overlooking a small village with two old friends studying the valley and mulling over events with a glass of wine

Oxford Dictionary 1987 definitions
Swarm (swawm) n. 1 a large number of small animals, people etc., esp. when moving in a confused mass.

"The wine is good",
The two old friends were seated comfortably in the bower of 'The Heights' overlooking the valley and the village below.
"Indeed" said James, "It is from our own grapes, we were lucky that some of the vines survived"
"Well it is good indeed, no matter whose feet did the treading" Michael exclaimed, "I have always favoured the local wine myself". Indeed, his lips were stained red, an indication perhaps of the amount he had drunk.
James took a sip, set down his glass and gazed into the distance. He frowned,

turned to Michael and said, "Do you hear that?"

Michael looked at him, "No" he replied shortly. James raised a sardonic eyebrow. Everyone knew that his friend was deaf. "Where?"

James looked across the bower and down the valley, "There, along the valley floor".

There was a pause while both men addressed their wine.

"There", said James again, "I can see dust".

"Oh yes, down to the left"

A faint haze seemed to be rising, slightly obscuring the lower road which led to the village.

"I can feel it too", Michael paused, "Have you your binoculars?"

"Yes, Jean, can you get my glasses please?"

Jean brought out the binoculars, James put it to his eye and peered down into the valley.

"There is a dark mass coming along the road, spilling out to either side".

"I CAN hear them now and, feel that tremor, let me see" Michael took the offered glasses, "By the Gods, it's a swarm!"

"A swarm?" said Jean,

"Yes, it's people, thousands of people. The dispossessed. The swarm. It moves forward constantly; boundaries are no deterrent. They cannot stop moving for to stop is to die. Like locusts they devour everything in their path and leave desolation behind them"

"God knows you are right. I recall now, they started years ago as refugees moving from country to country looking for a place to settle. Driven on each time by the armies of those lands until they took on a life of their own".

"They have gone through the lands of the East and spread into the Western countries of Europus, even moving across the seas when the bodies of the drowned washed up on the shores around".

Michael looked thoughtful, "We should be safe up here, not in a direct line of the swarm, they could pass by for hours yet".

The front of the swarm was now clearly visible, a vast mass of people moving almost at a run and spreading out to either side of the road. Then the leaders hit the first of the village houses. There came a growl of sound, a low rumble that echoed up the valley. A cloud of dust rose up, obscuring the front onslaught of the swarm. "You either join and run with them or they will consume you along with everything in their path" exclaimed James.

The swarm moved on through the village, consuming and destroying as it went. On and on it rolled, relentless in its movement like a wave, always flowing forward, never ebbing. The outriders were channelled through the side streets, taking - never stopping long enough to enjoy. The weight of the people coming on behind would not let them. Consume or die.

It was around four hours before the last stragglers came in sight. The old, the weak, the sick; gradually losing ground, passing through the swarm moving slower and slower until at last they were spat out at the end, staggering, gradually starving and dying. The path of the swarm was marked by the corpses of the fallen.

"By God", James looked upon the ruins of what had been a substantial village. The dust was gradually settling over the remains of houses, shops and the detritus of a swarm on the move. The stench of their passing had not yet reached the friends and as they gazed on the devastation below, more wine was called for and drunk to try and blot out their memories.

"Volunteers for burial squad" came the call.

Dictionary Amendment (Year 5 New Era)
Swarm; The. A mass of people unstopping, forever moving forward. A destructive force. First noticed during the movement of refugees across the Continent during the 2000's.

Burial party. An opportunity to get extra rations and a seat, (more importantly a voice), on the Council. The two friends trudged down to the village and joined the team around the local fore-man.

They collected their spades and walked along in silence to the farthest village boundary, about a klick from the centre, in order to start work. There was not much disturbance to be seen this far out, bushes and small trees flattened after being stripped of all useful nourishment. People had learned to keep anything of value buried as the swarm never stayed long enough to dig, only to destroy.

The bodies were the usual mix of the very old, the very young and those crippled by the continual movement.

"Hope they get the wagon down here more quickly this time, the heat won't do these much good"

"No, anything worth recycling on your side?" Michael looked around at bodies scattered along the trail.

"No" said James, "Everything worn to rags." The first thing you noticed was, no shoes. Then a lack of clothing, rags mostly, perhaps less than that on some of them, just a cloth and string to preserve whatever modesty they had left or perhaps just to keep the delicate areas covered from the dust and heat.

The younger ones had even less. But no-one lusted after young flesh any more. Worn down by lack of food and the constant movement, these were the remnants, the dross and rubbish left behind by the swarm. To be covered up as swiftly as possible before they rotted and contaminated what was left of civilisation! 'Civilisation', a word, a description of something that appeared to be rapidly disintegrating. We were 'Civilised'. We didn't eat our dead (yet) and we kept up the practices of our parents and their parents before them, that is to say, we did not kill each other unnecessarily! We ploughed the fields and scattered all right, we ploughed in the remains of the swarm and scattered their ground down bones as fertiliser!

Like them, we wasted nothing. We could not afford to. Waste was death. How had this happened? How did we fall so far from a society of countries and cities, towns, villages, a way of life that now seems so far gone that only the old, those that have survived that is, seem to remember?

Civilisation! A word. Civilised, be good to your neighbour. Respect others not only your own people, your own religion, your own sexual orientation. So many facets of society to be 'civilised' to and now? Now can be summed up by 'Watch thy neighbour' and if he falters, be prepared to enter his home and strip it clean. Look after the poor widow for when she dies, you can be first to search for her hidden trove. That, my friends, is civilisation. Eat or be eaten. Not literally of course, we leave that particular barbarism to the swarm, just figuratively, by keeping an eye on the main subject, one's own survival.

I have survived, keeping my eyes on the main chance and plunging in to look after my own interests but I would like to think that I have not lost all my humanity. So I remember. I remember when this all began. My memories direct or those of others passed to me in tales? A bit of both I would say, who now could take fact from fiction anyway?

Back in the early 2000's (old reckoning), wars and conflict seemed to span the

globe. Those that had refused to share with those that had not. Those at 'peace', turned away from those at war and so were sowed the seeds of our destruction.
In those glory days (to us at any rate) we spanned the continent of Europe. My wife and I, travelling like so many others, from Holland through Germany and on to those Eastern countries which had laboured so long under the religion of 'Communism'. I think it would have been around 2015 or '16 that the world first started noticing a movement of large numbers of people across Europe. I can remember seeing pictures of long columns of the 'dispossessed' (as they were called then) stretching through the Eastern European countryside. There appeared to be no goal save for that of reaching a country that would take them in, feed and clothe them and give them work. Yet there appeared that no country, (except Germany originally) was willing to accept not just the hundreds of thousands of the now, but the uncounted millions poised to march later.
Little did we know, or should I say rather that our leaders knew, just how devastating would be the result of slamming the doors. One country after

another sealed its borders, in the East of Europe, the old ways came to the fore with barbed wire and machine guns. We shall never know how many died then, thousands of men, women and children bulldozed into great pits and buried. But it didn't stop the movement of people. After a while it appeared that nothing would. Even the most brutal amongst us tires of killing and shamefacedly shoulders his weapon, marching away to his home town or village.

The fences eroded, the guards (except for the most obstinate) had gone, the way was open and the swarm started to take shape. The movement of large numbers of the dispossessed moved across the land, swallowing up what had been left. Then the different streams of people started to split because where one had passed, there was nothing for the next wave to take up and use. There came the need to move faster, to get the possessions of what was left before the next wave and so was born The Swarm. Ever moving, never stopping to rest. To stop was to starve and die. Movement was all and you faltered at your peril.

And so we fell. We? Yes, we the 'civilised'. We, the ones who were static. Who *remained where we were placed, 'home', that's where we stayed. To protect what was ours, to survive, to live as best we could while the Swarm moved through the country, the Continent, the World, never stopping, never ceasing to destroy in order to live. Was their motivation any different to ours? I don't know but not much I would say. All we do now is grow our crops, bury our goods and pray to whichever Gods we happen to worship that the Swarm passes us by.*

Christopher Wyatt 30/04/2016

While working at a pizza parlor I observed a man ordering a small pizza to go. He appeared to be alone and the cook asked him if he would like it cut into 4 pieces or 6. He thought about it for some time then said 'Just cut it into 4 pieces; I don't think I'm hungry enough to eat 6 pieces.

They Walk Among Us!

Twas the night before school started when all through the town, the teachers were groaning ... a disturbing sound! By 10 they were washed and tucked up in bed, where memories of children filled them with dread! New pencils, new folders new registers too! New classes, new grey hairs their anxiety grew.The parents just giggled when they learned of this fright, "you've had 6 weeks off. They're all yours, tough shite !

It's a Goal

Football mates wrapped
in scarves and coats shiver
in the stands, cradling tepid
Bovril whilst balancing pies,
dripping scalding meat.
Defeats suffered over pints
and post-mortem expletives.

But a goal gives green light
to their embrace, a kiss
planted on quiet neighbour's
bald pate, piggy back ride
from dour pensioner in front.

Work on Monday, small smile
and nod between the men,
both knowing the score.

Email: richard@seal2244.fsnet.co.uk
Tel: (0034) 622 299 367

**

My sister has a lifesaving tool in her car
which is designed to cut through a seat belt
if she gets trapped. She keeps it in the boot of the car.

They Walk Among Us!

Another one of Percy's Blogs and a caution about Bank Statements!

The Carbon Paper Scam. Now that we can talk to our banking facility every day even if it is only through a computer, at least it is possible to check your statement daily, which one should because if there is an error then you can normally have it put right immediately.

Let me tell a little story about fraud which at one time was quite rife way back in the days when secretaries and clerks used that clattering machine, the typewriter. It would be mostly women who would spend all of the working day punching out letters, but first they had to feed a sheet of paper into the carriage and normally two sheets of carbon paper to produce copies of the work. Let's take the Ford Motor Company, but then it could be any large organization. It does not take too much of an imagination to think of the masses of letters and the copies this company would produce every day, it must have run into the hundreds of thousands, letters to dealers and suppliers and of course customers.

Now some bright spark thought it was a good idea to send them an invoice for carbon paper and it became known as the 'Carbon Paper Scam'. It went on for a long time until auditors picked it up, for you see the invoices were for small amounts so nobody ever checked them, they just paid them, not realizing there was no order given for the stock and in fact there was no stock. It was reported the organizers of the scam got away with over a million pounds.

I'll go back to bank statements and cannot help but feel that maybe some organizations are doing something similar to its customers. Let me explain. Three years ago we took out an agreement with a software company to pay them twenty three pounds per year on the due date of February.

Each year since then the payments have gone through as agreed. However this year they decided to take a second payment in May. If we did not check our bank statement every day, we would not have known about it and they would be that much richer and us that much poorer.

This is not the first time this has happened, on another occasion it was over one hundred pounds that had been wrongly debited. The point really is was it deliberate or just a computer hitch – either way it pays to check. Why daily you may ask, well if there is a debit that should not be there then you can stop it there and then, if you leave it to the next day it is too late the bank will have paid it. On one occasion we found a thousand pounds was missing but I think we would have noticed that anyway. **I wonder how many people are having money debited as a regular payment, *which they know nothing about?***
Take care! **www.percychatteybooks.com**

**

Mist

Mist descends blotting
out sun, picking
out tree branches
to entangle, birds
to stifle, bushes to
smother, rich colours
of land to mute.
Like a blanket, mist
drapes slowly over
mountain tops, tucked
in tightly for the night.

Email: richard@seal2244.fsnet.co.uk
Tel: (0034) 622 299 367

An actual tweet from Chicago:

"I thought my vasectomy would keep my wife from getting pregnant but, apparently it just changes the color of the baby."

**

Racism!

Everyone seems to be in such a hurry to scream 'racism' these days, for instance:

A customer asked, "In what aisle could he find the Irish sausage?" The assistant asks, "Are you Irish?"

The guy, clearly offended, says, "Yes I am. But let me ask you something. If I had asked for Italian sausage, would you ask me if I was Italian?
Or if I had asked for German Bratwurst, would you ask me if I was German?
Or if I asked for a kosher hot dog would you ask me if I was Jewish?
Or if I had asked for a Taco, would you ask if I was Mexican?
Or if I asked for Polish sausage, would you ask if I was Polish?"

The assistant says, "No, I probably wouldn't."
The guy says, "Well then, just because I asked for Irish sausage, why did you ask me if I'm Irish?"

The assistant replied, "Because you're in Halfords."

Health and Safety

With grateful thanks to Pete Broadbent+

I wonder how Nelson would have fared on Trafalgar Day if he had been subject to modern day political correctness ... and our health and safety regulations?

***If he'd been alive today, he'd probably wonder why he ever bothered* If.**

The following sketch was performed at a Royal British Legion Christmas Party 2016.

Imagine. We are on the quarterdeck of HMS Victory. The weather is fine and to the south-east of us is amassed the fleet of Johnny Foreigner, who are hell bent on trouble. Admiral Nelson has ordered the hoisting of his now famous flag signal ...

Nelson: 'Hold on Captain Hardy, that's not what I ordered. What's the meaning of this?'
Hardy: 'Sorry sir. We have to do things in accordance with the rules.'
Nelson: 'But.'
Hardy: Your message now reads 'England expects every person to do his or her duty, regardless of race, gender, sexual orientation, religious persuasion, mental or physical disability.'
Nelson: What gobbledegook is that?'
Hardy: 'Admiralty policy sir. We're an equal opportunities employer now.'
Nelson: 'Gadzooks, Hardy. Hand me my pipe and tobacco.'
Hardy: 'Sorry sir. All naval vessels have now been designated smoke-free.'

Nelson: 'In that case, break open the rum. Let us splice the blasted main-brace to ready the men for battle.'
Hardy: 'The rum ration has been abolished, Admiral.'
Nelson: 'Good heavens, Hardy. Give me full speed.'
Hardy: 'I think you'll find that there's a 4 knot speed limit in this stretch of water.'
Nelson: 'Damn it man! We are on the eve of the greatest sea battle in history. We must advance with all dispatch. Let me have a report from the crow's nest.'
Hardy: 'That's not possible, sir. Health and Safety have closed it down. The rigging doesn't meet access regulations. It's out of bounds until a European approved scaffolding can be erected.'
Nelson: 'Whatever next? Give me full sail. The salt spray beckons.'
Hardy: 'A number of problems there sir. Health and Safety won't let the crew up the rigging without hard hats, safety harnesses and the correct footwear. Then we have to comply with the previously mentioned European directives for scaffolding.'
Nelson: 'I've never heard such effin rubbish. Open the ports and load the guns. Tell the men to stand by to engage the enemy.'
Hardy: 'The men are a bit worried about shooting at anyone Admiral. I should also warn you about regulations regarding bad or offensive language in the workplace.'
Nelson: 'What? This is effin mutiny!'
Hardy: 'It's not that, sir. We have a couple of legal-aid lawyers on board, watching everyone like hawks.'
Nelson: 'Then how are we to sink the enemy?'
Hardy: 'Actually, sir, we're not. Until article 50 is triggered, the enemy are our European partners. According to the Common Fisheries Policy, we shouldn't even be in this stretch of water.'
Nelson: 'But we all must hate Johnny Foreigner as we hate the devil Hardy.'

Hardy: 'I wouldn't let the ship's diversity co-ordinator hear you saying that sir.'
Nelson: 'We must consider, every man who speaks ill of us, to be our enemy.'
Hardy: 'Not any more, sir. We must be inclusive in this multicultural age. Now put on your Kevlar vest; it's the rules. It could save your life'
Nelson: 'Don't tell me - health and safety. Whatever happened to rum, sodomy and the cat-o-nine tails?'
Hardy: As I explained sir, rum is off the menu! And there's a ban on corporal punishment.'
Nelson: 'What about sodomy?'
Hardy: 'I believe that is now legal, sir.'
Nelson: 'In that case ... kiss me, Hardy.'
Anon

**

Piece of Cake

We ran out of rain
into crowded cafe's
cosy condensation.
Our legs entwined
in tight corner booth;
Luxuriated in lemon
drizzle, shared, with
Earl Gray. Fell in love,
got lost lingering over
tea bags squeezed.

Email: richard@seal2244.fsnet.co.uk
Tel: (0034) 622 299 367

**

Why isn't the number 11 pronounced onety-one?

If 4 out of 5 people SUFFER from diarrhoea...does that mean that one out of five enjoys it?

This Percy blog was written before the English June referendum 2016 and he insists there is nothing political about it he's just doing the numbers.

Softly, softly to catch a monkey. It is an old East End of London saying, and it does not mean catching small apes. It refers to selling an item or conning someone into buying something they do not want.

So my guess is we are all monkeys as it has taken the European Union forty odd years to sell us the idea of forming a federal state. Even now it is a group so powerful it dwarfs truly elected and patriotic countries, also even at this stage of development it is in control of all our lives – and by all I mean the member States in the whole of Europe who are supporting it.

There have been many monetary figures banded around about the cost, let me try and simplify it. We are told Britain pays three hundred and fifty million pounds a week to be in this club, which in return it tells the people how to live, what to buy, health and safety laws which ban ancient traditions, churning out draconian laws to enforce them. 350,000,000 pounds a week is a figure difficult to understand the real size and immensity of it.

Let's break it down. There are about twenty million families in the U.K. so that works out each family paying seventeen pounds fifty per week or 910 pounds a year to send to the E.U. If, and I hope when, the June vote takes place it is to leave this organization, then we will all be financially better off. Each family can be monetarily more secure, their shopping bill at the supermarket will be that much lower and each and every ones wage packet will go that much further.

We have lived in Spain for over fifteen years so we are not allowed to vote in this referendum, and people ask why I am so enthusiastic about Britain leaving? Because I believe the European Federal State will come to an end and everyone in this vast continent will be better off. One more thing, why do they want a European Army? Isn't that what the Third Reich developed in the early thirties and look where that led. **PercyChatteybooks@gmail.com**

**

Family isn't always blood.
It's the people in your life who want you
in theirs; the ones who accept you for
who you are. The ones who would
do anything to see you smile, and
who love you no matter what.

ANON

**

Bingo Billie

Ever since first visit
with Auntie Lil, hands
huge, bosom vast, dress
flowers all-encompassing,
Billie belonged to bingo.
Giggled with the girls over
two fat ladies, lads wave
winking over Woodbines.
Over decades dearest
departed, Billie remained
One Little Duck always,
eyes down for full house.

Email: richard@seal2244.fsnet.co.uk
Tel: (0034) 622 299 367

That about sums it up'

**

Mosquito

Lying awake, my head
aches, nerve breaks
awaiting dread return
of the whine, malign
high-pitched sure sign
of mosquito. Light on,
he disappears, playing
on fears through night
of his bite - no telling
how bad the swelling.

Email: richard@seal2244.fsnet.co.uk
Tel: (0034) 622 299 367

The Black Venus

The Black Venus is a small Inn in the wilds of Exmoor in Devon. Percy thought it may be fun to imagine how the name came about. For Venus in Roman mythology means God of Love – so why Black? He will take you back to a time when the world was totally different – it is the sixteenth century.

A dark night early spring 1649

The twin mast schooner battled its way through the heavy swell of the waters off the south coast of England as it headed for the small inlet, known as The Venus Cove. The cove, a wide deep water opening in the coastline was large enough to allow the keel of the sailing ship to pass safely over the mud below and anchor safely. The Captain had sailed into this small waterway a lot of times and was aware of its many dangers. To the front of the vessel, the navigating officer was casting a knotted line forward over the bow, measuring the depth of the water, whilst the master was shouting orders to the sailors controlling the rigging, to lower the sails, so that the ship would slow to an acceptable forward movement.

To one side stranded on the mud banks were the remains of a smaller vessel than the one now navigating into the small cove. He, the captain, had known the senior officer and most of the crew and had seen them as friends of what was now little more than an empty wreck. That was all before the ill fated night the ship was steered too close to the shore never to leave it again. When the Kings Revenue Men arrived accompanied by soldiers on horseback, the crew, who were smuggling barrels of wine were caught red handed and following a brief fight the poorly equipped sailors were overwhelmed and those not killed were taken for trial. The grounded vessel relieved of its stock was left to rot.

Over the years the old craft had been vandalised and most of her fittings had been removed. Some of the timbers of the stricken vessel had been stripped for use on other ships, in other instances materials to help build the small houses where the local fishermen lived. One part of the wreck remained because of superstition and the bringing of bad luck. That part was the carved coloured figurehead at the bow, of a lady in flight - her arms outstretched with the name Venus below her, the name of the old timber built ship, and the name the small inlet was to become known by.

The crewmen were rushing around the wooden decks preparing ropes to be used to secure the craft in the small bay when it came to rest. Another team were releasing ropes securing barrels and crates tied firmly to the decks, moving them to the edge where they could be off loaded on to small rowing boats which were coming out from the shore to meet the newcomer.

The shore men a lot earlier in the day had posted lookouts high in the hills above the inlet. Others were patrolling the small lanes around the area fearful of the Revenue men. The small boats from the shore were tying up alongside the new arrival. From the decks the burly sailors were lowering the kegs of spirit to handlers in the smaller craft and when full they pushed away from the ship. These little boats heavily laden, the water lapping at the gunnels, were propelled by oarsmen to the small wooden landing stage where a line of donkeys were waiting, each with bags of wool to be illegally exported.

Once the barrels from the ship had been transferred to the shore where the animals had waited patiently and the bales of wool were loaded in return, it was time for the vessel to put to sea. The unloading and the exporting of the other goods had taken longer than expected and the Captain knew he had been longer than he wished to be in the small cove and was anxious to get moving away from the area. On shore another group of men lead the donkeys, now laden with a barrel to each flank, up the gravel surfaced path away from the deep water inlet.

As they approached the end of the cove the path became steeper the surface rutted and not very firm under foot as it followed the small river that flowed into the bay. A little further on the path was becoming very steep and where the water fell over rocks from the higher ground, a waterfall formed as the water cascaded down the incline and foaming as it reached the bottom. The men leading the donkeys needed to encourage them by pulling them and pushing them up the gradient.

They followed the river nestling in the valley between the woodlands of the surrounding hills. As the sun started to appear over the horizon the smugglers made camp and lightened the loads on the animals settling down and waiting for the cover of darkness before continuing their journey inland to the small inn. Here their goods would be collected; in return they would receive payment for their work. After which, with nothing more to do, they would wait for news of the arrival of another vessel.

The Inn was really only a small stone building where they were heading, although only a few miles in from the sea, it would take the men with the donkeys more than two nights to reach it. The first sighting for them as they came over the brow of a hill was to see it settling in a small hamlet next to the river that they had been following. It was surrounded by tall old oak trees, their branches shading the stone built structure, which was the largest building in this small group of dwellings, used not only for merriment but also as a place where the community could meet.

The old oak panelled door with a crude hand - written sign above it declaring it to be The Venus, itself named after the rotting craft way down in the bay, where some of the fittings and timbers had been used to build the village room. The four smugglers pushed open the door and entered the space, a long open area with a dirt floor and a ceiling so low they had to bow their heads. Fixed into small alcoves in the walls oil lamps gave off a yellow light which cast eerie shadows around the walls.

To one end a log fire blazed in the grate of the large fireplace with stone seats built into the walls to its sides where on cold nights people could sit out of the draughts in the room. At the opposite end was a long table which acted as the bar. The owner, a lady in her thirties wore a flared skirt which dragged on the floor at her feet. It was she who now ran 'The Venus' after losing her husband to the dreaded disease of smallpox a few years before.

The four men were given a warm welcome by the merry makers in the room and jugs of ale were put before them which they quickly swallowed. A regular customer known for his musical and singing skills bent over from the chair where he was sitting and lifted a string instrument on to his lap and started strumming as he sang a popular melody, the people around him clapping in time.

A short time later having quenched their thirst, the band of men went outside to unload the animals carrying the contraband goods into the stone built store. The dark grey thatched roof a striking contrast to the clay red tiles of the bar.

The merriment and celebrations went on late into the night. A few women came from their small cottages to help with the laughter and in some cases to help husbands and boyfriends home to a blissful night of deep sleep in their drunkenness.

It had been a lot earlier when by chance two Revenue Men, whose job it was to patrol the area, had seen the line of donkeys making their way along a little used footpath to the hamlet. They had dismounted from their steeds and while one kept the horses quiet the other followed the line of animals and men making sure of their destination. Convinced they had not been seen they rode off to get support from a garrison of soldiers to arrest the men and the people in the small village who were involved in this Capital Crime against the King.

Not many of the revellers heard the sound of the troops coming as they galloped along the poor roads leading to the hamlet. A few who heard the noise of the hooves pounding the ground sat up where they were sleeping. Horror in their minds as they remembered what happened to smugglers when caught; leaping from their beds and escaping into the surrounding country side. Others were not quick enough and stood their ground drawing swords to fight off the intruding forces, the drink and lack of sleep hindered their chances of fighting off the Kings Men, and those that resisted arrest were killed where they stood. The Revenue Men were more interested in the bar and its contents; they had brought two wagons with them each drawn by two strong horses to confiscate the merchandise.

They marched into the bar searching cupboards, turning over tables, in their search for the illegal goods. In the small room at the back they found the landlady. She was cuddled up to one of the smugglers. The man tried to put up a fight but the Revenue Man shot him with a pistol he pulled from his belt the ball from the gun entering his heart killing him instantly.

Two of the heavily built men dragged the owner from her bed pulling the screaming woman into the bar, her feet dragging on the dirt floor; pushing her down they tied her to a chair. Making sure she was secure they left her while they went outside to count the barrels and to supervise the loading of the wagons. The soldiers had rounded up some of the men and women who had not escaped. They were lined up with their arms tied behind their backs, the ropes cutting into their skin as they were all linked together in a line.

The Revenue men who had been trying for some time to find the source of the contraband goods which had been entering the area, and being sold far and wide, sat to one side to work out what the next step was to be. They were determined to stop this smuggling racket. From the group four of them, two more had joined when the original two had gone for reinforcements, three wanted to destroy the small village there and then. The fourth argued that they should arrest them and take them into the Garrison town of Houghton, where they would be tried in a court. The three got their way and they decided to hold the court straight away.

With the owner still tied and sitting on the chair they formed a circle sitting on benches in front of her. They explained they worked for and represented the King of the land and they had the authority to stamp out all activities concerning smuggling. The hearing only took a few minutes, after which they took her outside put her on a horse with a rope around her neck tied to the oak tree. The horse was whipped across its flanks from which it bolted. The owner of The Venus was left hanging.

The soldiers marched the remainder of the people away, leaving the small village empty and left to the wilds of nature.

In the course of time the bar reopened, a new road had been built from the town of Houghton by a business man who saw the opportunity of developing the small bay. The old stone bar would be on the new route and the new occupier developed it, the old sign was still hanging above the door but knowing something of it history, he changed the name and called it The Black Venus.

Taken from the novel 'The Black Venus' by Percy Chattey

WHEN I WAS A LAD

By Tony Brown

WHEN I WAS A LAD MUSIC HAD A RING TO IT
IT HAD RYTHM, WITH A SWING TO IT
A MELODY, YOU COULD SING TO IT
BACK WHEN I WAS A LAD

OUR MUM USED TO COOK ALL OUR DINNERS AND TEAS
THERE WERE NO READY MEALS OR THINGS THAT YOU FREEZE
WE'D NEVER EVEN HEARD OF MACKIE D'S
NOT WHEN I WAS A LAD

THE WAR WAS OVER, PEACE HAD BEGUN
WE WEREN'T TOO SURE JUST WHO HAD WON
WE NEEDED COUPONS FOR A CURRANT BUN
OR A ROLL

THERE WERE SHORTAGES WHEREVER YOU'D LOOK
FROM THINGS FOR THE HOUSE TO THINGS THAT YOU COOK
EVEN YOUR CLOTHES WERE ON POINTS IN A BOOK
HOW DROLL

ONCE A YEAR WE'D PACK OUR THINGS,
OUR SWIMMING TRUNKS, OUR WATER WINGS

AND OTHER STUFF LIKE RUBBER RINGS
TO GO ON OUR VACATION

WE DIDN'T JUMP ABOARD A PLANE
AND TRAVEL OFF TO SUNNY SPAIN
WE CLIMBED INTO A SOOTY TRAIN
ON LIVERPOOL STREET STATION

NO EXOTIC VENUE COULD WE AFFORD
ONLY THE RICH COULD GO ABROAD
ON BRIGHTON BEACH WE THANKED THE LORD
WE'D REACHED OUR DESTINATION

NO POSH HOTEL WITH STARS OF THREE
NO VIEWS ACROSS THE SPARKLING SEA
NO, MRS BILTON'S B AND B
WAS WHERE WE LAID OUR HEADS

NO SINGING AFTER NINE AT NIGHT
NO HOT WATER OR ELECTRIC LIGHT
AND CERTAINLY NO PILLOW FIGHTS
OR JUMPING ON THE BEDS

WHEN SEVEN DAYS HAD BEEN AND WENT
AND ALL OUR POCKET MONEY SPENT
WE'D LOOK BACK ON THE GRAND EVENT
AND SHED A SILENT TEAR
FOR ONCE WE GOT ABOARD THAT TRAIN
WE KNEW ONE THING FOR SURE WAS PLAIN
WE'D NOT BE COMING HERE AGAIN

FOR AT LEAST ANOTHER YEAR

WE DIDN'T GET TAKEN TO SCHOOL IN A CAR
TWO MILES WAS CONSIDERED "NOT VERY FAR"
IF YOU DIDN'T HAVE A BIKE, WELL THERE YOU ARE
YOU JUST HAD TO WALK

WE DIDN'T CALL OUR TEACHERS MARY OR JACK
IT WAS MISS OR SIR AND NO ANSWERING BACK
WE WERE THERE TO LEARN AND THAT WAS THAT
WE HARDLY DARED TO TALK

WHEN SCHOOL WAS OVER WE PLAYED WITH OUR MATES
AND WE CHATTED OVER OUR GARDEN GATES
IF WE WERE LUCKY WE EVEN HAD SKATES
AND WE SKATED

AS WE GOT OLDER THOUGH STILL QUITE TENDER
WE BEGAN TO TAKE NOTICE OF THE OPPOSITE GENDER
I REMEMBER I HAD A CRUSH ON A GIRL CALLED BRENDA
AND WE DATED

BUT IT DIDN'T LAST SO IT WAS BACK TO THE BLOKES
WE ALL HUNG AROUND TELLING TERRIBLE JOKES
AND I GOT ME A BIKE, IT WAS MISSING SOME SPOKES
BUT I RODE IT

I REMEMBER WHEN TV CAME ONTO THE SCENE
IT WAS JUST ROUND THE TIME WHEN WE GOT A NEW QUEEN
AND WE WATCHED HER GET CROWNED ON A NINE INCH SCREEN
WHEN THEY SHOWED IT

WE DIDN'T HAVE PAGERS OR MOBILE PHONES
WITH OBSCENE OR MUSICAL RINGING TONES
IF WE WANTED TO SPEAK TO WILLIAMS OR JONES
WE JUST MET THEM

COKE WAS SOMETHING WE BURNED IN THE GRATE
A FIX YOU WERE IN WHEN YOU GOT IN A STATE
JOINTS WERE THE MEAT THAT WE HAD ON OUR PLATE
AND WE ATE THEM

ALL OF OUR SHOPS PLIED A DIFFERENT TRADE
FROM SIX INCH NAILS TO LEMONADE

MOST OF THEIR GOODS WERE "BRITISH MADE"
AND WE BOUGHT THEM

SUPERMARKETS WERE YET TO APPEAR
TO DRIVE OUT THE SHOPS THAT WE HELD SO DEAR
WE DIDN'T REALLY WANT THEM HERE
AND WE FOUGHT THEM

COMPUTER GAMES OF THESE WE'D NONE
NEW TECHNOLOGY HAD NOT BEGUN
WE USED TO MAKE OUR OWN CLEAN FUN
WITHOUT IT

BUT PROGRESS MUST PREVAIL WE'RE TOLD
AND ALL THAT'S NEW REPLACES OLD
IS ALL THAT GLISTENS ALWAYS GOLD
I DOUBT IT

NOW I'M NOT SAYING THINGS WERE ALWAYS BRIGHT
OR THAT EVERYTHING WAS SWEETNESS AND LIGHT
THERE WERE HARDSHIPS THAT WE HAD TO FIGHT
BUT WE MANAGED TO COPE

THINGS WOULD GET BETTER BEFORE TOO LONG
COMMUNITY SPIRIT WAS VERY STRONG

IF WE STUCK TOGETHER WE COULDN'T GO WRONG
AND WE LIVED IN HOPE

WELL THINGS DID GET BETTER OR SO THEY SAY
JUST LOOK AT HOW LUCKY WE ARE TODAY
OUR FREEDOM IS STEADILY MELTING AWAY
BUT WHAT CAN WE DO

THIS WORLD OF P C HAS GONE STARK RAVING MAD
YOUNG CHILDREN CAN´T EVEN CUDDLE THEIR DAD
I THINK I WAS HAPPIER WHEN I WAS A LAD
HOW ABOUT YOU

**

Yellow 24

A man goes into a doctor's office feeling a little ill The doctor checks him over and says, 'Sorry, I have some bad news, you have Yellow 24, a really nasty virus.
It's called Yellow 24 because it turns your blood yellow and you usually only have 24 hours to live.
There's no known cure so just go home and enjoy your final precious moments on earth..'
So he trudges home to his wife and breaks the news.
Distraught, she asks him to go to the bingo with her that evening as he's never been there with her before.
They arrive at the bingo and with his first card he gets four corners and wins $35.
Then, with the same card, he gets a line and wins $320
Then he gets the full house and wins $5000.
Then the National Game comes up and he wins that too getting $780,000.

The bingo caller gets him up on stage and says, 'Son, I've been here 20 years and I've never seen anyone win four corners, a line, the full-house and the national game on the same card.
You must be the luckiest bastard on Earth!'
'Lucky?' he screamed. 'Lucky? I'll have you know I've got Yellow 24'.
'F___k me,' says the bingo caller. 'You've won the meat raffle as well

**

JUST BEFORE I WAS DEPLOYED TO IRAQ, I SAT MY EIGHT-YEAR-OLD SON DOWN AND BROKE THE NEWS TO HIM. "I'M GOING TO BE AWAY FOR A LONG TIME," I TOLD HIM. "WHY?" HE ASKED. "DON'T YOU KNOW THERE'S A WAR GOING ON OVER THERE?"

Students at a local college were assigned to read two books, "Titanic" and "My Life" by Bill Clinton.

They were asked to do a book report and contrast the 2 books. One student turned in the following book report with the proposition that they were nearly identical stories!

Titanic: Cost = $29.99
Clinton : Cost = $29.99

Titanic: Over 3 hours to read
Clinton : Over 3 hours to read

Titanic: The story of Jack and Rose, their forbidden love, and subsequent catastrophe.

Clinton : The story of Bill and Monica, their forbidden love, and subsequent catastrophe.

Titanic: Jack is a starving artist.

Clinton : Bill is a bullshit artist.

Titanic: In one scene, Jack enjoys a good cigar.

Clinton: Ditto for Bill

Titanic: During the ordeal, Rose's dress gets ruined.

Clinton : Ditto for Monica's.

Titanic: Jack teaches Rose to spit.

Clinton : Let's not go there.

Titanic: Rose gets to keep her jewellery.

Clinton : Monica is forced to return her gifts.

Titanic: Rose remembers Jack for the rest of her life.

Clinton : Clinton doesn't remember anything.

Titanic: Rose goes down on a vessel full of seamen.

Clinton : Monica.. Ooh, let's not go there, either.

Titanic: Jack surrenders to an icy death.

Clinton : Bill goes home to Hillary; basically the same thing.

His professor gave him an A+

**

Life is too short to wake up in the morning
with regrets.
So, love the people who treat you right
and forget about the ones who don't.
And believe
that everything happens for a reason...
if you get a chance - take it;
if it changes your life - let it.
Nobody said that it would be easy...
They just promised
it would be worth it.

YOUR GOD'S PLAN FOR AGING

Most seniors never get enough exercise. In His wisdom God decreed that seniors become forgetful so they would have to search for their glasses, keys and other things thus doing more walking. And God looked down and saw that it was good.

Then God saw there was another need. In His wisdom He made seniors lose coordination so they would drop things requiring them to bend, reach & stretch. And God looked down and saw that it was good.

Then God considered the function of bladders and decided seniors would have additional calls of nature requiring more trips to the bathroom, thus providing more exercise. God looked down and saw that it was good.

So if you find as you age, you are getting up and down more, remember it's God's will. It is all in your best interest even though you mutter under your breath.

Nine Important Facts To Remember As We Grow Older

9. Death is the number 1 killer in the world.

8. Life is sexually transmitted.

7. Good health is merely the slowest possible rate at which one can die.

6. Men have 2 motivations: hunger and hanky panky, and they can't tell them apart. Lady if you see a gleam in his eyes, make him a sandwich.

5. Give a person a fish and you feed them for a day. Teach a person to use the Internet and they won't bother you for weeks, months, maybe years

4. Health nuts are going to feel stupid someday, lying in the hospital, dying of nothing.

3. All of us could take a lesson from the weather. It pays no attention to criticism.

2. In the 1960's, people took LSD to make the world weird. Now the world is weird, and people take Prozac to make it normal.

1. Life is like a jar of jalapeno peppers. What you do today may be a burning issue tomorrow.

.

**

Five Minute Management Course

Lesson One :

A man is getting into the shower just as his wife is finishing her shower, when the doorbell rings. The wife quickly wraps herself in a towel and runs downstairs. When she opens the door, there stands Bob, the next-door neighbour.

Before she says a word, Bob says, 'I'll give you €800 to drop that towel.'

After thinking for a moment, the woman drops her towel and stands naked in front of Bob, after a few seconds, Bob hands her €800 and leaves.

The woman wraps back up in the towel and goes back upstairs. When she gets to the bathroom, her husband asks, 'Who was that?'
'It was Bob the next door neighbour,' she replies.

'Great,' the husband says, 'did he say anything about the €800 he owes me?'

Moral of the story:
There comes a time when greed must be paid for.

Lesson Two:

A priest offered a Nun a lift, She got in the car and crossed her legs, forcing her gown to reveal a leg. The priest nearly had an accident. After controlling the car, he stealthily slides his hand up her leg.

The nun said, 'Father, remember Psalm 129?'

The priest removed his hand. But, after changing gears, he let his hand slide up her leg again.

The nun once again said, 'Father, remember Psalm 129?'

The priest apologized 'Sorry sister but the

flesh is weak.' Arriving at the convent, the nun sighed heavily and went on her way.

On reaching the church, the priest rushed to his rooms to look up Psalm 129. It said, 'Go forth and seek, further up, you will find glory.'

Moral of the story:
If you are not well informed in your job, you might miss a great opportunity.

Lesson Three:

A sales rep, an administration clerk, and the manager are walking to lunch when they find an antique oil lamp.

They rub it and a Genie comes out. The Genie says, 'I'll give each of you just one wish. 'Me first! Me first!' says the admin clerk. 'I want to be in the Bahamas, driving a speedboat, without a care in the world.' Puff! She's gone.

'Me next! Me next!' says the sales rep. 'I want to be in Hawaii , relaxing on the beach with my personal masseuse, an endless supply of Pina Coladas and the love of my life.' Puff! He's gone.

'OK, you're up,' the Genie says to the manager.

The manager says, 'I want those two back in the office after lunch.'

Moral of the story:
Always let your boss have the first say.

Lesson Four

An eagle was sitting on a tree resting, doing nothing. A small rabbit saw the eagle and asked him, 'Can I also sit like you and do nothing?'
The eagle answered: 'Sure, why not.'

So, the rabbit sat on the ground below the eagle and rested. All of a sudden, a fox appeared, jumped on the rabbit and ate it.

Moral of the story:
To be sitting and doing nothing, you must be sitting very, very high up.

Lesson Five:

A turkey was chatting with a bull. 'I would love to be able to get to the top of that tree' sighed the turkey, 'but I haven't got the energy.'

Well, why don't you nibble on some of my droppings?' replied the bull. They're packed with nutrients.'

The turkey pecked at a lump of dung, and found it actually gave him enough strength to reach the lowest branch of the tree. The next day, after eating some more dung, he reached the second branch.

Finally after a fourth night, the turkey was proudly perched at the top of the tree. He was promptly spotted by a farmer, who shot him out of the tree.

Moral of the story:
Bull Shit might get you to the top, but it won't keep you there..

Lesson Six:

A little bird was flying south for the winter. It was so cold the bird froze and fell to the ground into a large field. While he was lying there, a cow came by and dropped some dung on him.

As the frozen bird lay there in the pile of cow dung, he began to realize how warm he was. The dung was actually thawing him out!

He lay there all warm and happy, and soon began to sing for joy. A passing cat heard the bird singing and came to investigate. Following the sound, the cat discovered the bird under the pile of cow dung, and promptly dug him out and ate him.

Morals of the story:

(1) Not everyone who shits on you is your enemy.

(2) Not everyone who gets you out of shit is your friend.

(3) And when you're in deep shit, it's best to keep your mouth shut!

THUS ENDS THE FIVE MINUTE MANAGEMENT COURSE

Who Cares?

I was standing at the bar one night minding my own business. This FAT ugly chick came up behind me, grabbed my behind and said, "You're kinda cute. You gotta phone number?"

I said, "Yeah, you gotta pen?"

She said, "Yeah, I got a pen". I said, "You better get back in it before the farmer misses you."

Cost me 6 stitches but when you're almost seventy...who cares?

****

Cowboy: "Give me 3 packets of condoms, please." Lady Cashier: "Do you need a paper bag with that, sir?" Cowboy: "Nah. She's purty good lookin'." When you're over seventy...who cares?

****

I was talking to a young woman in the bar last night. She said, "If you lost a few pounds, had a shave and got your hair cut, You'd look all right."
I said, "If I did that, I'd be talking to your friends over there instead of you."
Cost me a fat lip but, when you're over seventy...who cares?

****

I was telling a woman in the pub about my ability to guess what day a woman was born just by feeling her breasts.
"Really" she said, "Go on then. Try."
After about thirty seconds of fondling she began to lose patience and said, "Come on, what day was I born?"
I said, "Yesterday."
Cost me a kick in the nuts, but when you're over seventy...who cares?

****

I got caught taking a pee in the swimming pool today. The lifeguard shouted at me so loud, I nearly fell in. Cost me a bloody nose. But when you're over seventy...who cares?

****

I went to the pub last night and saw a BIG woman dancing on a table. I said, "Good legs."
The girl giggled and said, "Do you really think so?"
I said, "Definitely! Most tables would have collapsed by now."
Cost me 6 more stitches. But when you're over seventy...who cares?

Ruin

Atop a hill aside
from expat villas sits
the ruin, tumble-down
walls, ceiling collapsed,
living room decorated
with rock piles, shadow-
ghosts drift past holes.
Who lived here? Birds
on bits of roof answer
wind whispers in
forgotten corners.

Email: richard@seal2244.fsnet.co.uk
Tel: (0034) 622 299 367

**

Wallace

Wallace walked into a supermarket with his zipper down. A lady cashier called out to him and said, "Your barracks door is open." Not a phrase that men normally use, he went on his way looking a bit puzzled. When he was about done shopping, a man came up and said, "Your fly is open." He zipped up and finished his shopping. At the checkout, Wallace intentionally got in the line where the lady was who told him about his "barracks door." He was planning to have a little fun with her, so when he reached the counter he said, "When you saw my barracks door open, did you see a Marine standing in there at attention?" The lady, who was a bit sharper than the man, thought for a moment and said, "No, no, I didn't. All I saw was a disabled veteran sitting on a couple of old Duffel bags"

**

Bus Tour

Groups of Americans were traveling by tour bus through Holland.

As they stopped at a cheese farm, a young guide led them through the process of cheese making, explaining that goat's milk was used. She showed the group a lovely hillside where many goats were grazing. 'These' she explained, 'Are the older goats are put out to pasture when they no longer produce.'

She then asked, 'What do you do in America with your old goats?'

A spry old gentleman answered, 'They send us on bus tours!

**

Kids Are So Honest

WHILE I SAT IN THE RECEPTION AREA OF MY DOCTOR'S OFFICE, A WOMAN ROLLED AN ELDERLY MAN IN A WHEELCHAIR INTO THE ROOM. AS SHE WENT TO THE RECEPTIONIST'S DESK, THE MAN SAT THERE, ALONE AND SILENT. JUST AS I WAS THINKING I SHOULD MAKE SMALL TALK WITH HIM, A LITTLE BOY SLIPPED OFF HIS MOTHER'S LAP AND WALKED OVER TO THE WHEELCHAIR. PLACING HIS HAND ON THE MAN'S KNEE, HE SAID, "I KNOW HOW YOU FEEL. MY MOM MAKES ME RIDE IN THE STROLLER TOO."

**

AS I WAS NURSING MY BABY, MY COUSIN'S SIX-YEAR-OLD DAUGHTER, KRISSY, CAME INTO THE ROOM. NEVER HAVING SEEN ANYONE BREAST FEED BEFORE, SHE WAS INTRIGUED AND FULL OF ALL KINDS OF QUESTIONS ABOUT WHAT I WAS DOING. AFTER MULLING OVER MY ANSWERS, SHE REMARKED, "MY MOM HAS SOME OF THOSE, BUT I DON'T THINK SHE KNOWS HOW TO USE THEM."

**

OUT BICYCLING ONE DAY WITH MY EIGHT-YEAR-OLD GRANDDAUGHTER, CAROLYN, I GOT A LITTLE WISTFUL. "IN TEN YEARS," I SAID, "YOU'LL WANT TO BE WITH YOUR FRIENDS AND YOU WON'T GO WALKING, BIKING, AND SWIMMING WITH ME LIKE YOU DO NOW.
CAROLYN SHRUGGED. "IN TEN YEARS YOU'LL BE TOO OLD TO DO ALL THOSE THINGS ANYWAY."

**

WORKING AS A PEDIATRIC NURSE, I HAD THE DIFFICULT ASSIGNMENT OF GIVING IMMUNIZATION SHOTS TO CHILDREN. ONE DAY, I ENTERED THE EXAMINING ROOM TO GIVE FOUR-YEAR-OLD LIZZIE HER INJECTION.
"NO, NO, NO!" SHE SCREAMED.
"LIZZIE," SCOLDED HER MOTHER, "THAT'S NOT POLITE BEHAVIOR."
WITH THAT, THE GIRL YELLED EVEN LOUDER, "NO, THANK YOU! NO, THANK YOU!"

**

ON THE WAY BACK FROM A CUB SCOUT MEETING, MY GRANDSON INNOCENTLY SAID TO MY SON, "DAD, I KNOW BABIES COME FROM MOMMIES' TUMMIES, > BUT HOW DO THEY GET THERE IN THE FIRST PLACE?" AFTER MY SON HEMMED AND HAWED AWHILE, MY GRANDSON FINALLY SPOKE UP IN DISGUST, "YOU DON'T HAVE TO MAKE UP SOMETHING, DAD. IT'S OKAY IF YOU DON'T KNOW

**

Teacher "Maria go to the map and show where North America Is." Turning to the class she asks "Now who discovered North America?"
A little boy in front says "Maria did."

HIS WIFE'S GRAVESIDE SERVICE WAS JUST BARELY FINISHED, WHEN THERE WAS A MASSIVE CLAP OF THUNDER, FOLLOWED BY A TREMENDOUS BOLT OF LIGHTNING, ACCOMPANIED BY EVEN MORE THUNDER RUMBLING IN THE DISTANCE. THE LITTLE, OLD MAN LOOKED AT THE PASTOR AND CALMLY SAID, "WELL, SHE'S THERE."

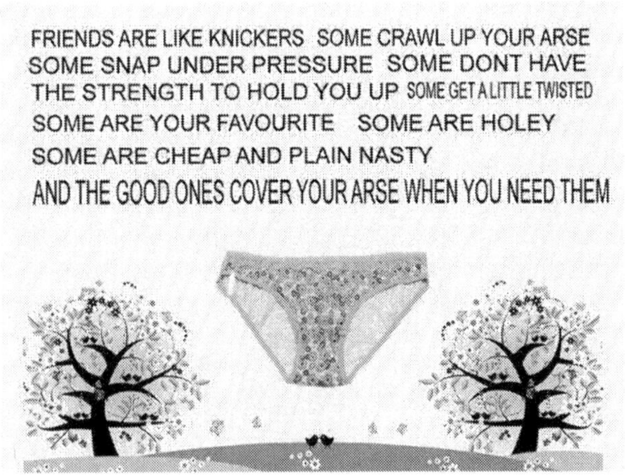

FRIENDS ARE LIKE KNICKERS SOME CRAWL UP YOUR ARSE SOME SNAP UNDER PRESSURE SOME DONT HAVE THE STRENGTH TO HOLD YOU UP SOME GET A LITTLE TWISTED SOME ARE YOUR FAVOURITE SOME ARE HOLEY SOME ARE CHEAP AND PLAIN NASTY AND THE GOOD ONES COVER YOUR ARSE WHEN YOU NEED THEM

A Noble Deed

So a man dies and goes to heaven, and when he gets there he is approached by St Peter who asked "what in your opinion was your most noble deed?"

"Uh, well I saw some huge bikers harassing an old lady outside a bar once, so I went up to the biggest balding guy and ripped his nose ring off."

Peter was impressed and asked "Well done when did this happen?"

"About five minutes ago!"

**

While looking at a house, my brother asked the Real Estate agent which direction was north because He didn't want the sun waking him up every morning. She asked, 'Does the sun rise in the north?' My brother explained that the sun rises in the east And has for sometime. She shook her head and said, 'Oh, I don't keep up with all that stuff......'
They Walk Among Us!

**

One night, an 87-year-old woman came home from Bingo to find her 92-year-old husband in bed with another woman..

She became violent and ended up pushing him off the balcony of their 20th floor apartment, killing him instantly.

Brought before the court, on the charge of murder, she was asked if she had anything to say in her defense. 'Your Honour,' she began coolly, 'I figured that if at 92, he could screw, he could fly.

**

The Balkan

Ever since the Eighteenth century and before, conflicts in the group of countries known as the Balkan Peninsula have taken place, most of which were disputes over land borders. Some of which became serious conflicts from time to time, especially in the periods of the Balkan Wars and the First and Second World Wars. A long while before that, the Romans had first invaded the area in 160BC it was part of their Empire for almost one hundred years. Since that time the area has been in constant conflict

and it has not been unknown for people to be massacred in their hundreds over land or religious disputes, one of which took place in the later time of 1999.

In the last one hundred years the security forces in each region have been involved in trying to form a peaceful solution between the warring parties, but from time to time outside military forces have been involved in trying to quell the unrest amongst the various countries which later became known as Yugoslavia This the first chapter from Percy's book 'The Black Venus'

The small ancient village nestling in the valley of a mountain range - part of this community clung to the side of a steep hill with a paved main road leading up and finally out of the area, the surface of which had cracked and split over the years through lack of repair. About two hundred metres up this road was a turning on the right hand side, on the corner of which stood an old run down red brick detached house. In its prime, three hundred years before, it would have belonged to a wealthy merchant who had traded in the area. The current occupiers were the third generation to live in the property as it was passed down through the male side of the family, but times had changed and the family had fallen on hard times.

The side road was little more than a track - unpaved and rutted from the traffic that used it to reach the houses further up the hill, the mud from the road running out onto the road junction. On the right hand side of the track was a long old dirty red brick wall, the pointing peeling away adding to its shabbiness. On the other side of this two metre high boundary wall the noise of hens clucking could be heard and through a wire gate the unkempt area could be seen with a poorly maintained chicken house at one end of the yard, and a dilapidated shed beside it. At the other end of this area, a rear door to the house, wide open despite the chill in the air, but a closer look showed that it had not been closed for a long time as the top hinge was broken and the outer edge was touching the ground.

Most of the house was now dirty and had not been decorated for years. Just off the yard was a rundown kitchen with a wood burning stove for cooking, a broken porcelain sink stained brown by the cold water dripping tap, also shelving along the walls. There were two more rooms off the kitchen, one of which would have been a very grand dining room a long time before.

Further on towards the front of the property, there was the main room, this had also lost its splendour from what was once a very well tastefully furnished living room. Now the curtains were filthy and torn, the windows with so much grime and dirt on them that it was impossible to see clearly through them. To the inner wall a large stone surround fireplace with two very old and badly stained grubby arm chairs in front of it. There was a small fire trying to establish itself in the grate the little flames lapping around the wet logs that had been used to light it.

Anna Pasha, a small lady was wearing a badly worn out old army great coat which was too long, so that besides her head, the only other part of her that could be seen was the dirty flat black shoes which had seen too much wear to be comfortable any longer. She struggled out of the house in which she had lived all her married life, through the old door with blistered paint work leading on to the street. The door was a struggle to close as it also scraped the floor where the hinges had become worn. Lowering her head she started to walk down the hill wearing a dark blue woollen hat offering very little protection against the drizzling rain.

She struggled down the street with a large canvas bag in one hand, because of its size it occasionally dragged along the ground. Anna was making her way to the market square where the stalls of traders were laid out with farm produce, and some of the merchandise was still in boxes straight from the fields.

The town's market was at the bottom of the hill. It covered the square at the centre of four roads. In the past the area had been levelled so, to one side, steps led up to the trading area. Stalls of all sizes and shapes were arranged in rows selling not only food, but other items required for the home. Some had separated wire fronted cages with rabbits or chickens inside, the hardware stall had been on the same corner since people could remember. Further down the row was a children's toy stall that also sold pushchairs, bedding and the like, with the used clothing stall next to it.

Some of the stalls had coloured bunting hanging from them trying to cheer up a dull, cold and wet day. To help them keep warm most of the sellers had small stoves so that, when they were not serving the few customers that were present, they would hold their hands over them. The stoves had various fuels, logs or coals making them glow from their heat in the muggy atmosphere of the square.

A little way from Anna's door, as she struggled down on the uneven pavement, a mud spattered dark green army jeep went past. She watched it as it slowed down and finally came to a stop. Two soldiers alighted from the vehicle and stood beside it. They wore different uniforms to the local army and were studying the activity of the stall holders, most of them were standing around waiting to serve customers and trying to warm their hands over the makeshift stoves. In the meantime others were busy especially on the food stalls serving people their daily needs.

She could not help wondering when it was all going to come to a stop. Ever since she could remember some form of fighting had taken place, people being killed over some small dispute and now foreign forces had been drafted in, in an endeavour to quell the disorder as another group of activists tried to overthrow the government.

At the bottom of the hill and just before entering the market, a small butchers shop stood on the corner of a row of retail premises. Anna entered the brightly lit area and ordered some cheap cuts of meat placing the wrapped package inside her bag.

Anna felt cold and stiff and was leaning forward as she made her way up the few steps to get to the first stall. She found herself a little out of breath. Looking round she saw the two soldiers watching her. She could hear someone running and then a man bumped into her nearly knocking her over. She stumbled to one side and was aware he was putting his hand into her bag, she smiled to herself as there was nothing in there but a few scraps of meat, her money was safely tucked into her belt holding up her old dirty trousers below the heavy coat she was wearing.

She moved along the stalls looking for the few vegetables they would require for the evening meal, which she would cook for her husband Goren. She stopped and chatted a few times with some of the stall holders many of whom she had known for years. Whilst talking she would be warming her hands over their stove, and thinking to herself that the meat suddenly feels heavy, but she put that down to age.

For some reason she felt very uncomfortable, she could not help the feeling of being watched. It was not until reaching Carla, who was dressed almost identically except for the piece of string tied around her waist. Thirty years previously the two had been great friends and used to attend the same school together. Her friend said to her with a grin on her face, "There's a soldier not far behind you, he must fancy you as he has been watching you and seems to be very interested in what you are doing."

"I don't know what he wants, I've got nothing, and also I've nothing to hide. He came down the road past our house in one of those jeep things."

Anna looked round wondering where the other soldier was, and then she saw him at the far end of the market where she had entered it. He had stopped the man who had put his hand into her bag, she thought to herself serve him right for trying to steal from an old lady.

At the vegetable seller she said, "Got anything cheap today Carla?" She was walking around the stall as she said it. "Goren's not feeling too good this morning and a bowl of hot broth with a little bit of meat in it would do him the world of good."

From behind her a voice boomed, "Woman is that some form of code?"

She was surprised at the interruption and looked at her old friend shrugging her shoulders, "Is he talking to you?"

Before Carla could reply the voice said, "I'm talking to you - the one with the bag, what have you got in it?"

Anna was suddenly very frightened, now that he had mentioned the bag; she thought to herself once again, it feels different as if it were heavier.

She looked around her wanting to run, she had never been in trouble with the police or the army before, why was he following her?

She was grabbed on the arm by the soldier snatching the bag from her, and then she knew there was something in it as it swung to his side. That cannot be possible, it was empty when she left home and she had only bought a little meat. A feeling of horror came over her, that man he was not trying to take something out but he was putting something in.

The soldier put his hand into the bag and brought out a small revolver, a nasty black looking thing which he was holding by the barrel. She was looking up at him as he was a lot taller than her. She was stuttering as she said, "I don't know where that came from."

He grabbed her arm. "You are coming with us. We've already got the other one you were working with."

A feeling of being in deep trouble came over her. How was she going to explain that she had nothing to do with it? Would anybody understand and believe her that you can carry a gun round and not know it is there? Anyway it was a very small gun, and when you have pains in your arms and legs you are more worried about them than what is in your bag.

He was treating her roughly pulling her along the path between the stalls. She was dragging her feet as she could not keep up with his long strides. Stallholders she had known for years, some since she was a child, were shouting "Leave her alone" and banging boxes and anything that would make a noise.

Through her tears she saw another army jeep arrive. The man who had given her all this trouble was being bundled into it. She was sobbing "Please don't take him away I want to talk to him." The soldier just ignored her and continued towards the other vehicle.

They arrived at the jeep where another soldier was waiting who had the three chevrons of a Sergeant on his arm. By now the crowd had started to follow and were becoming menacing. Someone from the rear tossed a stone which bounced off the kerb in front of the soldiers.

The two men pushed Anna into the jeep manacling her wrist to the vehicle and quickly drove off. The stall holders were no match for their speed as they pulled away, but nevertheless a group of them started to follow.

The army jeep stopped outside her house. Releasing her hands they dragged her from the vehicle. One of them stood to the side of the front door - a machine gun in his hand and kicked the door open moving in ready to spray the inside with bullets if there was a need. But there was no response - just a frightened old man looking at them with his hands held out to a small fire in a grate where he had been trying to keep warm.

The Sergeant, holding a pistol in his hand which he had drawn from a holster on his army belt, shouted to the soldier that had first entered the house. "Get upstairs and make sure it is clear." He pushed the woman inside, "You sit over there." She sat in a chair close to the fire where in normal times she spent most of her life knitting or exchanging the odd word with her husband.

The third man said "The CO is coming, he is just coming up the hill" At that moment an army staff car pulled up behind the Jeep.

Goren had stood up and moved behind the chair he had been sitting on. "What is going on? There is nothing here for you people." There was a look of horror on his face and he was trembling trying to hold on to the back of the chair.

"Shut up." The Sergeant replied. They could hear the footsteps above them from the one who had gone up to the bedrooms and crashing noises as he was searching the rooms.

The Colonel pushed his way into the door, the Sergeant turned round to greet him. "Hello Sir, with respect Sir why are you here?"

"I was just passing Sergeant and saw the commotion. What is happening"?

At that moment Anna leaning to one side reached to the side of the chair. The Sergeant seeing the movement out of the corner of his eye turned and fired the revolver he was holding in his right hand, the noise echoing around the room, rattling the windows, dust rising from the neglected furniture.

Goren was horrified the noise of the shot echoing in his ears. He saw the Sergeant turning the gun towards him. He turned, stumbled, as he made for the door to the rear room. The gun went off again and he felt a tug at his arm. Fear drove him forward and out of the house. He hid in the old shed certain that they would find him.

Out in the street the crowd which had followed from the market and had been shouting, stopped. Suddenly everything went very quiet as they looked at each other wondering what had happened.

The Colonel instructed one of the soldiers to go out and control the crowd. He looked at the Sergeant, "I think we have a problem?"

Anna had slumped forward - the blood pumping out of a wound in her back.

The Sergeant looked at his superior officer and said, "She was reaching behind the chair - she must have been going for a gun...The old man he's escaped through that door. Where is he?" In the confusion and the noise no one had followed to see where he had gone.

"We had better recover the weapon she was reaching for." The Colonel, followed by the Sergeant walked over to where Anna had been sitting beside the stone fireplace.

The two soldiers walked around the back of her chair expecting to find a firearm, there was nothing, but hanging to the side in front of the fire was a set of Rosary Beads. The two men looked at each other. "Earlier on, you said when you picked her up in the market she had a gun, go and get it and put it in her hand, and let's get out of here. We will call the local police and tell them that she tried to shoot you."

The crowd had been following up the steep hill and were angry, two of the leaders were trying to attack the car the CO had arrived in and were being held back by two soldiers with bayonets fixed to their rifles, and with a sigh of relief they heard the order to leave.

The soldiers filed out of the house and quickly climbed into their vehicles and sped away going up the hill away from the crowd of market people, which by now had swollen in numbers.

When the first of the crowd went into the room they found Goren leaning over his wife rocking her gently and crying.

From 'The Black Venus' by Percy W. Chattey

**

Devious:

A man in Scotland calls his son in London the day before Christmas Eve and says, "I hate to ruin your day but I have to tell you that your mother and I are divorcing; forty-five years of misery is enough."

'Dad, what are you talking about?' the son screams.

"We can't stand the sight of each other any longer" the father says. "We're sick of each other and I'm sick of talking about this, so you call your sister in Leeds and tell her."

Frantically, the son calls his sister, who explodes on the phone. "Like hell they're getting divorced!" she shouts, "I'll take care of this!"

She calls Scotland immediately, and screams at her father "You are NOT getting divorced. Don't do a single thing until I get there. I'm calling my brother back, and we'll both be there tomorrow. Until then, don't do a thing, DO YOU HEAR ME?" and hangs up.

The old man hangs up his phone and turns to his wife. 'Sorted! They're coming for Christmas - and they're paying their own way.'

**

The Toast

Murphy drops some buttered toast on the kitchen floor and it lands butter-side-up. He looks down in astonishment, for he knows that it's a law of nature of the universe that buttered toast always falls butter-down.

So he rushes round to the presbytery to fetch Father Flanagan. He tells the priest that a miracle has occurred in his kitchen. But he won't say what it is, so he asks Father Flanagan to come and see it with his own eyes.

He leads the priest into the kitchen and asks him

what he sees on the floor."Well," says the priest, "it's pretty obvious. Someone has dropped some buttered toast
on the floor and then, for some reason, they flipped it over so that the butter was on top."
"No, Father, I dropped it and it landed like that!" exclaimed Murphy
“Oh my Lord," says Father Flanagan, “dropped toast never falls with the butter side up.....It's a mir....Wait... it's not for me to say it's a miracle. I’ll have to report this matter to the Bishop and he'll have to deal with it. He’ll send some people round; to interview you, take photos and a statement etc.”
A thorough investigation is conducted, not only by the archdiocese but by scientists sent over from the Curia in Rome, Italy. No expense is spared. There is great excitement in the town as everyone knows that a miracle will bring in much need tourism revenue.
Then, after 8 long weeks and with great fanfare, the Bishop announces the final ruling.“It is certain that some kind of an extraordinary event took place in Murphy's kitchen,(quite outside the natural laws of the universe). Yet the Holy See must be very cautious
before ruling it a miracle. All other explanations must be ruled out. Unfortunately, in this case, it has been declared ‘No Miracle’ because they think that
Murphy may have buttered the toast on the wrong side!”

Percy's Blog.

Percy wrote this in December 2016 and was current at the time however IT IS worth repeating.

The main problem of getting old is worrying about it. One dreads getting to seventy and then when you are past it you breathe a sigh of relief and then after half a dozen years you start worrying about being eighty. When you are past it then you stop worrying because you made it.

I see the people that control the police are continuing looking into sexual occurrences that may or may not have happened by Ted Heath when he was a leading light in political circles also Prime Minster back in the nineteen fifties. The fact he is dead is of no consequence so I am not sure what they are looking to prove, and if they do what they are going to do with it. I would have thought their time would be better spent finding out why, when he was P.M. he was allegedly allowed to deceive the British public by illegally signing documents that took the U.K. into the Common Market. Would it not be more useful to find out why the Parliament and the legal profession of the time allowed it to happen.

Evidently if you get on a bus these days you cannot pay in cash you have got to have one of the bus company's prepayment cards. Great for the company, they have your money up front before providing the service. There is the story of a regular traveller leaving his card at home and the driver and conductor of the bus allowed him to travel without paying because they were not allowed to accept money, although he had offered it to them. That was fine until an Inspector got on to check tickets. Again the traveller explained his difficulty and the employees confirmed that they had allowed him to travel. He offered to pay the three pound twenty pence fare, which was refused because the Inspector also could not accept cash. The man was taken to court and fined 700.00 pounds. Be careful when you go out make sure you have got your wallet with you.

www.percychatteybooks.com

**

The Stella Awards for 2015

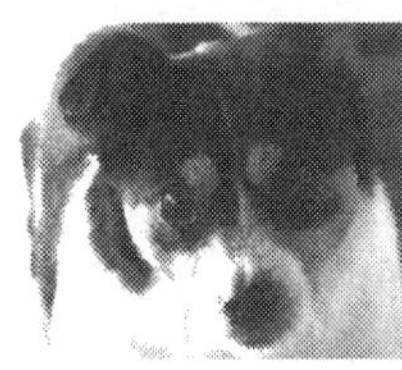

With grateful thanks to the Stella Awards committee. For those unfamiliar with these awards, they are named after 81 year old Stella Liebec who spilled hot coffee on herself and successfully sued McDonalds in Mexico where she had purchased the coffee. She had taken the lid off the coffee and put it between her knees while driving. Who would ever think one would get burned for doing that, right?

These awards are for the most outlandish Law suits, and verdicts in the United States.

Seventh Place

Kathleen Robertson of Austin Texas, was awarded $80,000 by a jury of her peers after breaking her ankle tripping over a toddler who was running in a furniture store. The store owners were understandably surprised by the verdict, considering the running toddler was her own child.

Sixth Place

Carl Truman, 19, of Los Angeles, California won $74,000 plus medical expenses when his neighbour ran over his hand with a Honda Accord. Truman apparently did not notice there was someone at the wheel of the car when he tried to steal his neighbours hub caps.

Fifth Place

Terrence Dickson, Bristol, Pennsylvania who was just leaving a house he had just burgled by way of the garage. Unfortunately for him the automatic garage door opener malfunctioned and he could not get it to open. Worse he could not re-enter the house because the door had locked when Dickson had pulled it shut. Forced to sit for eight DAYS and survive on a case of Pepsi and a large bag of dog food, he sued the homeowners' insurance company claiming undue mental anguish. Amazingly the jury ordered the insurers to pay him $500,000 for his anguish.

Forth Place

Jerry Williams, Little rock, Arkansas was awarded $14,000 plus medical expenses after being bitten on the butt by his next door neighbours beagle – even though the beagle was on a chain in its owners fenced yard. Williams did not get as much as he asked for because the jury believed the dog might have been provoked when Williams had climbed over a fence into the yard and repeatedly shot the dog with a pellet gun.

Third Place

Amber Carson, Lancaster, Pennsylvania a jury ordered a Philadelphia restaurant to pay her $113,500 after she slipped on a spilled soft drink and broke her tailbone. The reason the soft drink was on the floor Ms Carson had thrown it at her boyfriend 30 seconds earlier during an argument.

Second Place

Kara Walton, Claymont, Delaware sued the owner of a night club in a nearby city because she fell from the bathroom window to the floor knocking out her two front teeth. Even though she was trying to sneak through the ladies room window to avoid paying the $3.50 cover charge., the jury said the night club has to pay $12,000 plus dental expenses.

FIRST PLACE!

This is unbelievable: Mrs Merv Grazinski, Oklahoma City, Oklahoma purchased a new 32 foot Winnebago motor home. On her first trip home from a football game and driving on the freeway, she set the cruise control at 70 MPH and calmly left the driver's seat to go to the back of the motor home to make a sandwich. Not surprisingly the motor home left the freeway, crashed and turned over. Mrs Grazinski sued

Winnebago for not putting in the owners manual that she couldn't actually leave the driver's seat while the cruise control was set.
She was awarded $1,750,000 plus a new motor home.

We understand Winnebago changed their manuals as a result of this suit, just in case Mrs. Grazinski has any relatives who might also buy a motor home.

**

Red Sky

Watching a red sky
at night, we willed
last embers, dying, to
ignite; grasping at
oranges, tried to hold
back pervading black
shrinking the pinks.
No sunrise seen next
morning - you passed
without warning.

Email: richard@seal2244.fsnet.co.uk
Tel: (0034) 622 299 367

**

The Winter Boots

(**Anyone who has ever dressed a child will love this**)
There was a teacher who was helping one of her pupils put on his boots? He asked for help and she could see why. Even with her pulling, and him pushing, the little boots still didn't want to go on. By the time they got the second boot on, she had worked up a sweat. She almost cried when the little boy said, ***'Teacher, they're on the wrong feet.'***
She looked, and sure enough, they were. Unfortunately, it

wasn't any easier pulling the boots off, than it was putting them on. She managed to keep her cool as together they worked to get the boots back on, this time on the correct feet.
He then announced, ***'These aren't my boots'***
She bit her tongue, rather than get right in his face and scream, like she wanted to. Grinning and looking at him saying **'Why didn't you say so?'**
Once again, she struggled to help him pull the ill-fitting boots off his little feet. No sooner had they got the boots off when he said,
'They're my brother's boots. But my Mom made me wear 'em today.'
Now she didn't know if she should laugh or cry. But she mustered up what grace and courage she had left to wrestle the boots BACK onto his feet again. Helping him into his coat, she asked,
'Now, where are your mittens?'
He said,
'I stuffed 'em in the toes of my boots...'

**

The Big Black Bra!

This is the story of three woman who meet in a bar one is engaged – another is a mistress to a wealthy business man – the other has been married for forty years.
They were chatting about relationships and decided to amaze their men by greeting them at the door by just wearing a Black Bra, stiletto heels and a mask and swapping stories later.

A few days later they all got together and the engaged girl explained her experience first. "When my boyfriend arrived home he found me wearing a black leather bodice, tall stiletto heels and a mask. Drooling at the mouth he murmured about loving me and took me into the bedroom and we made love all night long."

The mistress was next to tell what happened. "The other night I arrived at my lovers office wearing a raincoat under which I was only wearing a mask , a black bra and high heels. When I opened the raincoat he didn't say a word he just started to tremble and we had wild sex all night right there in his office."

The third was looking a little downcast when she said "I was like you two wearing a black bra and black stockings with my best stilettos and a mask. He came in the door put his things down and hanged up his coat and said 'What's for dinner' and went into the living room and put the television on."

**

The "W" in Christmas

Author Unknown

Each December, I vowed to make Christmas a calm and peaceful experience. I had cut back on nonessential obligations -- extensive card writing, endless baking, decorating, and even overspending. Yet still, I found myself exhausted, unable to appreciate the precious family moments, and of course, the true meaning of Christmas.

My son, Nicholas, was in kindergarten that year. It was an exciting season for a six-year-old. For weeks, he'd been memorizing songs for his school's "Winter Pageant." I didn't have the heart to tell him I'd be working the night of the production.

Unwilling to miss his shining moment, I spoke with his teacher. She assured me there'd be a dress rehearsal the morning of the presentation. All parents unable to attend that evening were welcome to come then. Fortunately, Nicholas seemed happy with the compromise. So, the morning of the dress rehearsal, I filed in ten minutes early, found a spot on the cafeteria floor and sat down. Around the room, I saw several other parents quietly scampering to their seats. As I waited, the students were led into the room. Each class, accompanied by their teacher, sat cross-legged on the floor. Then, each group, one by one, rose to perform their song.

Because the public school system had long stopped referring to the holiday as Christmas," I didn't expect anything other than fun, commercial entertainment - songs of reindeer, Santa Claus, snowflakes and good cheer. So, when my son's class rose to sing, "Christmas Love," I was slightly taken aback by its bold title.

Nicholas was aglow, as were all of his classmates, adorned in fuzzy mittens, red sweaters, and bright snowcaps upon their heads. Those in the front row-center stage -- held up large letters, one by one, to spell out the title of the song. As the class would sing "C is for Christmas," a child would hold up the letter C. Then, "H is for Happy," and on and on, until each child holding up his portion had presented the complete message, "Christmas Love."

The performance was going smoothly, until suddenly, we noticed her; a small, quiet, girl in the front row holding the letter "M" upside down -- totally unaware her letter "M" appeared as a "W." The audience of 1st through 6th graders snickered at this little one's mistake. But she had no idea they were laughing at her, so she stood tall, proudly holding her "W." Although many teachers tried to shush the children, the laughter continued until the last letter was raised, and we all saw it together. A hush came over the audience and eyes began to widen. In that instant, we understood the reason we were there, why we celebrated the holiday in the first place, why even in the chaos, there was a purpose for our festivities.

For when the last letter was held high, the message read loud and clear:

"C H R I S T W A S L O V E"

Traffic Camera

A man was driving when he saw the flash of a Traffic camera. He figured that his picture had been taken for exceeding the limit, even though he knew

that he was not speeding...
Just to be sure, he went around the block and passed the same spot, driving even more slowly, but again the camera flashed.
Now he began to think that this was quite funny, so he drove even slower as he passed the area again, but the traffic camera again flashed.
He tried a fourth time with the same result.. He did this a fifth time and was now laughing when the camera flashed as he rolled past, this time at a snail's pace... Two weeks later, he got five tickets in the mail for driving without a seat belt..
They walk amongst us!

**

Radio

As child, enjoyed magic
wireless fiddling - Dials
turned, twiddle twisted
through distant hisses;
the strange voices rising,
fade falling, then stalling.
Later, transistor helped
in fighting sleepless fret.
Now sound digital, same
solace at World Service,
joys galore with radio four;
can never feel downcast,
with shipping forecast.

 Email: richard@seal2244.fsnet.co.uk
Tel: (0034) 622 299 367

Just a Thought

Many years ago we used to visit a beautiful pub in the wilds of Challacombe on Exmoor in North Devon. By the lovely oak carved fireplace was a dark wooden chair on the back rest of the seat it said 'Bobs Chair' he was the oldest person in the village and at the time was in his nineties, nobody sat in that seat and if a stranger did he was told to move. Bob would make his way in during the evening and order his large scotch and sit by the fire drinking whilst nodding to everyone. I had visions of retirement meaning just that, sitting in a chair in the local bar nodding to everyone, I wanted more than that for the two of us and I understood that to get it would mean a complete change of life style. Moving to Spain has done just that, everything new with lots of things to learn, a weather which is normally very comfortable, new friends to meet from all walks of life most of whom are retired and have nothing to prove, giving us a totally relaxed life style.

**

A Doctor was addressing a large audience in Tampa, speaking from the lectern he says 'The material we put into our stomachs is enough to have killed most of us sitting here, years ago. Red meat is awful. Soft drinks corrode your stomach lining. Chinese food is loaded with MSG. High fat diets can be disastrous, and none of us realises the long-term harm caused by the germs in our drinking water. However, there is one thing that is the most dangerous of all and we all have eaten, or will eat it. Can anyone here tell me what food it is that causes the most grief and suffering for years after eating it?'

After several seconds of quiet, a 75-year-old man in the front row raised his hand, and softly said, 'Wedding Cake.'

The Swiss French Border

The opening chapter for Percy's novel 'Watchit' set in the mid nineteen fifties. Watchit because it concerns the smuggling of watches into the U.K.

The early morning sun was shining through the trees silhouetting the bare branches, which were showing the first signs of buds, promising very strong foliage for the summer months ahead. The trees were doing little to shield the strong rays from the driver of the Jaguar car as he made his way through the Swiss countryside, towards the border with France.

It had been just over an hour earlier, in the dawn of a new day, when Miles had left a small workshop in the back streets of an insignificant group of houses in a small hamlet, about an hours' drive from the border crossing with France. Hans, the tall broad shouldered German with a totally shaven head, had supplied the goods which were now well hidden in the car. As Miles drove away Hans's final words in guttural English rang in his mind, words which had been harshly said with a strong hidden meaning, '*Tell Charlie I don't want any delay in receiving payment for the merchandise like the last time. Tell him no later than Friday'*. Miles nodded his head, not liking the man - he was also fearful of him and he was glad to be on his way thinking it would give him three days to drive back to England.

The big car was sweeping forward past the road junction with the signpost telling the lone driver that there were six kilometres to the border. He drove on slightly nervous, very aware of how outstanding the car was in this part of Europe, barely twelve years after the end of the Second World War.

He was very familiar with the road and the route as this was the third time he had travelled it in the previous six months. The highway surface was in need of repair, and in places, it had been washed away by snow melting on the mountains with the resultant waters rushing down the foothills and on to the road using it as a drain.

The road curved to the right and through the trees he could see the buildings of the Swiss Customs post. His pulse started to race as he wondered if they would recognise him from his previous journeys. He started to sweat, his hands were making the steering wheel wet with his perspiration. He took deep breaths trying to calm down, forcing himself to drive the vehicle forward.

The Swiss Customs Officer walked out of the hut, saw the British number plates on the car and waved him through. He raised a shaking hand in acknowledgement, and drove the three hundred yards to the French post. The officer had seen him coming and had left his office to hold up his hand indicating for him to stop.

Miles stopped the car, wound down the window and then held the steering wheel as hard as he could, in an effort to stop his hands from shaking. The two officials inspected his papers. Both looked at him with suspicion and the smaller of the two walked to the front of the car beckoning him to open the bonnet. He leant across the car smelling the leather of the seats and groped for the release lever. Pulling it, there was a resounding 'bong' as the hood sprang open against the safety catch.

As he recovered his posture on the seat, the second officer opened his door. Terror struck him. It was like a very bad dream. People insisting he did things he did not want to do. He was conscious of the engine still running. Grabbing hold of the door, he tried to close it and at the same time, he slipped the car into gear. The uniformed official at the side of the car realized what he intended to do, and was trying to stop him. The driver's door was still slightly open and he reached through trying to grab hold of Miles.

Through the windscreen, he could see the other officer was still fiddling with the catch. He floored the accelerator pedal and the engine roared. Power surged to the rear wheels, which spun trying to find a grip in the loose gravel on the surface, stones being flung backwards. The car leapt forward – there was a scream, as the small Frenchman standing in front was pushed along by the powerful car. His legs were trapped under the front bumper while he tried to hold onto the top of the shiny slippery bonnet.

Still trying to fight off the officer at the door, the scream made him turn his head in time to see the stricken eyes staring from a face as it disappeared below the level of the radiator. There was a sickening thud and the vehicle jumped as it forced its way forward. Underneath there was a dragging sound and then nothing as the car shook itself free and surged forward.

The driver's door slammed against the arm of the Customs man and the increasing momentum of the car forced him to let go. However, the strap on his gold watch trapped him and he was dragged along the hardened road surface as the car gathered speed. The strap broke and the time piece dropped and became wedged by the seat. The officer fell heavily to the ground badly injured with grazes to his skin and broken bones. He managed to raise himself on to one knee and taking out his revolver fired after the car, but could only watch as it vanished around the first bend, sending loose stones dancing across the surface of the road beneath a slight haze of dust.

The opening Chapter of 'Watchit!'

**

The Wife

Bob, a 70-year-old, extremely wealthy widower, shows up at the Country Club with a breathtakingly beautiful and very sexy 25-year-old blonde-haired woman who knocks everyone's socks off with her youthful sex appeal and charm and who hangs over Bob's arm and listens intently to his every word. His buddies at the club are all aghast.

At the very first chance, they corner him and ask, 'Bob, how'd you get the trophy girlfriend?'

Bob replies, 'Girlfriend? She's my wife!'

They are knocked over, but continue to ask. 'So, how'd you persuade her to marry you?

'I lied about my age', Bob replies.

'What, did you tell her you were only 50?' Bob smiles and says, 'No, I told her I was 90.'

**

Like Father Like Son

Brenda and Steve took their six-year-old son to the doctor. With some hesitation, they explained that although their little angel appeared to be in good health, they were concerned about his rather small penis.

After examining the child, the doctor confidently declared, 'Just feed him pancakes. That should solve the problem.'

The next morning when the boy arrived at breakfast, there was a large stack of warm pancakes in the middle of the table. 'Gee, Mom,' he exclaimed. 'For me?'

'Just take two,' Brenda replied. 'The rest are for your father.'

**

The Fridge

Some guy bought a new fridge for his house.
To get rid of his old fridge, he put it in his front yard and hung a Sign on it saying: 'Free to good home. You want it, you take it.'
For three days the fridge sat there without anyone looking twice.
He eventually decided that people were too mistrustful of this deal. So he changed the sign to read: 'Fridge for sale $50.'
The next day someone stole it!
They walk amongst us!

**

Last Weekend

Friday

Standing beside the overflowing laundry basket, Miriam took a deep breath and exhaled slowly whilst considering for the umpteenth time whether to give up smoking. After a couple of minutes of silent seething, she started ironing her way through the pile of her husband's shirts and underwear. Before long, she sensed her vacant stare degenerating into a glare and could feel her nostrils flaring.

Miriam told herself, under her breath, to look after herself, to take care. She had a secret smile at the idea of gathering his garrulousness, placing all the put-downs and securing his sarcasm wrap-trapped into a tight ball then burying them all. However, given that he was not dead, all she could do was bide her time for now, hang on in there, seeing red.

Saturday

On a bright August morning, Miriam faced a familiar battle to rise from her depths beneath a blanket heavy with thick blackness. Floundering in the eye of a summer's morning storm, she cowered under floral covers. Eventually emerging, she blinked, battered, braced against her own stiff breeze with its chilly edge. It seemed like she had never felt the sun, and could only hope for cloud cover at best.

The nadir of a grim day spent in a fog was reached during a row with her teenage daughter. Unable to restrain her fury at the sight of the snarling girl, Miriam felt herself dying inside over banning stopovers and raging 'It's my rules when you're under my roof!' The younger woman had the last word saying that it was not her fault that her mother hated her husband and was bitter about relationships.

Sunday

Although she woke with the sinking sensation at the prospect of another dark day, Miriam felt a new determination to start wielding the will to fight, challenge the endless rounds of faulty thinking. Alone in the house for a few hours, this seemed like a good day for action, serious thinking and to start stopping drinking. Over breakfast, she managed to keep depression at bay, felt anxiety levels degrading into subtle shades of grey.

That evening, Miriam hummed to herself whilst preparing spaghetti Bolognese and salad, which she served to her family with her trademark sweet smile. She barely heard her daughter mumbling the usual grumbles, pouting pushing pasta and prodding her peppers. She did not care when her husband accepted his plate grudgingly, and seemed to enjoy finding fault with her sauce.

Miriam relished the final hours of her last weekend. She drank mineral water, enjoyed her main course and the home-made dessert that no one else wanted to share, then watched a weak comedy movie surrounded by sullen silence. To this day she has stayed bright breezy at the thought of her hidden bags, the taxi ordered for dawn, and note ready to leave on her departure. She left no forwarding address.

Email: richard@seal2244.fsnet.co.uk
Tel: (0034) 622 299 367

**

A Box of Condoms

The mother of a 17-year-old girl was concerned that her daughter was having sex. Worried the girl might become pregnant and adversely impact the family's status, she consulted the family doctor. The doctor told her that teenagers today were very wilful and any attempt to stop the girl would probably result in rebellion. He then told her to arrange for her daughter to be put on birth control and until then, talk to her and give her a box of condoms.

Later that evening, as her daughter was preparing for a date, the mother told her about the situation and handed her a box of condoms.

The girl burst out laughing and reached over to hug her mother, saying, 'Oh Mom! You don't have to worry about that! I'm dating Susan!'

**

A clearly inebriated woman, stark naked, jumped into a taxi in New York City and laid down on the back seat.

The cab driver, an old Jewish gentleman, opened his eyes wide and stared at the woman. He made no attempt to start the cab.

The woman glared back at him and said, "What's wrong with you, honey? - Haven't you ever seen a naked woman before?"

The old Jewish driver answered, "Let me tell you sumsing, lady. I vasn't staring at you like you tink; det vould not be proper vair I come from"

The drunk woman giggled and responded, "Well, if you're not staring at my boobs or ass, sweetie, what are you doing then?"

He paused a moment, then told her..."Vell, M'am, I am looking and I am looking, and I am tinking to myself, 'Vair in da hell is dis lady keeping de money to pay for dis ride?

Now, that's a real business man!

**

Charlie and Ian

A chapter from Percy's book 'Watchit'. To set the scene Ian had illegally arrived in Britain from France and now he has a need to go back without the authorities knowing.

It was a comforting feeling for Ian as Charlie brought the engines to life and the yacht made its way across the harbour towards the English Channel. There was a slight swell on the sea as the pair sat in the small cabin of the thirty-five foot craft. The twin diesel engines muffled below deck, driving the boat away from Ramsgate at a steady twelve knots.

Just prior to leaving the mooring, the harbour master had come alongside the yacht, standing on the dock, and advised them not to go out to sea because of the weather forecast. Charlie had assured him they were not going out far and just wanted to demonstrate to his friend how the boat performed. He was nodding to Ian as he said it.

They were about two miles out from the harbour and had planned to stop and start fishing in case there was a coastguard watching their movements. But there was no need, the visibility was very poor and had obliterated the coast. They continued on their way knowing that the direction they were taking made it impossible to be seen from the shore.

They watched as the wet and clammy air around them slowly closed in until it was very dark. "Ian this is a hopeless task. This is not the right chart and it tells me nothing. It doesn't even show the French coast. Anyway we should slow down, at this speed if we hit some flotsam it could do a lot of damage."

All he got by way of a reply was a grunt as his companion took a swig from the rum bottle, which was kept on board.

Charlie continued "I don't even know which way the tide is running to be able to navigate with any certainty. Lucky there is no wind to complicate the problem. You know son, this yacht only goes out in the sun so we can see our way back. This is bloody madness, sitting in the middle of the Channel, in thick fog with daylight turning into night just a few hours away."

Ian was not well up on navigation at sea. On land he was an expert. At least he thought they were going in the right direction. He tried to add something to the conversation, "Surely Charlie, if we head for Calais, we must get there? Anyway, I know you have taken it out at night before. Also you have got a compass that will show us the way, and bloody hell France is big enough, surely we can't miss it?"

"I know I have been out at night before but that was different and well planned. Without knowing the entire factors son that are affecting this little trip, we could end up anywhere if we don't get run down by a bloody great liner first. Look let me show you. " He spread out the coastal chart on the table. Pointing to a spot on it he said, "I know we are here, but without the other chart where is Calais?" Pointing again off the chart he said, "If it is here due East, then making a setting on the compass for 90 degrees and off we go and without taking other factors into account we should arrive there. But supposing it is here, then it is South East and we would then need to set the heading for something like 120, but on the other hand it could....well I am sure you understand."

"Why haven't we got the chart you need if we knew we were going to France?

"Ian we were in a rush as I remember when we left and because of all the hurry, I left it on the dining room table in the farm. I wasn't too worried when we were on the way because without this fog you can see the part of France you want and - it would have been easy."

"Oh, that was not very clever. It has been a long day and I've still got a long way to go. Anyway, I've got complete faith in your judgement."

Charlie smiled at his naivety. "You are a clown old son. You sit there as if you are sunbathing in the South of France without a care in the world."

"Sun bathing! What in this weather? At the moment I am relaxing ready for the arduous task ahead. Anyway what is the use of worrying?"

"Let's have something to eat - what time are you meeting Pierre?"

"He'll be in a hotel bar in the centre of Calais from about ten onwards. The name of the place is in my suit." Ian nodded his head towards the small cabin.

"At this rate he will have to wait a week before I get you there."

They got the basket of food out which they had brought with them and shared it out, "Don't worry if he said he will wait, that is what he will do."

"Well if he doesn't it will create one more problem – and I will have to hire a car and the trouble with that is it leaves a trail. A train will take too long"

They continued eating for a while, and then Ian said "By the way I gave him a thousand Francs for his trouble." Charlie looked at him with a blank stare, "Sodding hell Ian that is about one hundred pounds" – Ian felt uncomfortable. "Well, he wouldn't do it for nothing."

Ian took a mouthful of chicken, chewed for a while and said, "That reminds me the ex's on this job are exceeding expectation – let alone the time it is taking and the worry, but I'll settle for the Jaguar, providing I can get it back home in one piece."

Charlie didn't twitch a muscle. He looked at Ian to see if he was serious, and realised he was. "You are the greatest; you make a deal with me and then raise your cut. Not satisfied with that you get me out here in this fog filled hell and the middle of the bloody sea and ask for more." Now Charlie's vindictiveness wanted to hurt his colleague.

"It is mist Charlie, not fog." But Charlie was not listening and continued, "You don't care how much I'm making out of the deal – or how I am going to get back out of this....misty bloody hell."

"You do go on Charlie, and you said that without calling me 'son', an improvement. We should have brought some beer with us to go with this picnic as that rum is a bit clinging and dry in your mouth – anyway thanks for the car I have become very fond of it."

Charlie, sick by now that his friend had offhandedly demanded the Jaguar from him said casually, "Christine has got a beautiful body, very desirable in black lacy underwear with those lovely legs, but I did not know she was a virgin."

His words shocked Ian, and he choked on the chicken he was eating and stared at him. With his mouth still full he stuttered, "What do you mean 'WAS' a virgin'?"

"Well I thought all the time you have been with her she would have lost that a long time ago."

Ian was furious and threw the remainder of the food overboard, and was still staring. His heart was thumping and could feel the anger rising inside him. He leant forward. He grabbed hold of Charlie's arm squeezing it. "What are you trying to tell me Charlie?"

Charlie tried to pull his arm away, feeling stupid for telling Ian and then said, "Lay off me Ian - she came round to tell me you needed Chronicost, I think someone must have told her you had gone away with Pat – she was upset and well you know how these things happen. Anyway I didn't think you would care - we have shared women in the past."

Ian pushed him away, "You are a right bastard, of course I bloody care. She is very special to me and was not for sharing as you put it, I'm a good mind to give you a bloody good hiding." He paused and was thinking before continuing, "Where did you do it in the back seat of that fancy car....oh no....you didn't take her up to your mirrored seduction room." He saw the look on his companions face, "You did – didn't you? You are a bastard. Don't tell me you took pictures as well for your wall."

"Who knows...maybe next time?"

Ian let go of his arm, "Charlie there is not going to be a next time – and certainly no pictures, now you do understand me – don't you?"

"Maybe – anyway it is a bit late for the pictures, if you want them they will be ready by the time you get back."

"Sometimes I think you are a bit sick taking pictures of the women you take to bed."

"It's a hobby old son, something to dream over in my old age – and it makes a nice few bob on the side. I sell them through an agent and a lot go to the States some to Europe. Anyway I don't expect you were celibate while you've been away, with my dear Pat?"

"That is different...anyway what do you mean by 'My dear Pat'?" Suddenly Ian was seeing Charlie in a different light one which he was not sure he liked.

"It is not different. You go away and make sure you have some comfort with you, and leave your girlfriend on her own - so she needed comforting."

"I bet it was you who told her who I was with? Anyway I asked what you meant by 'My dear Pat'?"

"Well she comes round now and again to see me." Ian was a little surprised and very angry, he leant even further forward saying, "Oh! And what is now and again?"

"Ah! I don't know I expect it is about once a week. She especially likes going upstairs. But she insists on wearing a mask" He grinned at his shipmate, who looked at him in surprise as he did not realise Pat was involved. Charlie continued, "I think we had better concentrate on where we are going, also start keeping a look out for any ships that are passing this way."

"Alright Charlie, but I won't forget this in a hurry, and as I said leave Christine alone. Anyway how are we going to keep a look out as you put it in this thick fog?"

Charlie's response was, "You said it was mist – remember. The best way is keep your ears sharp for any noise."

Ian was not really listening. He was wondering what he was going to say to Christine when he saw her. He was furious with her, he had a feeling of revulsion and the magic had gone. Then he thought to himself '*perhaps Charlie was only kidding*'.

From the novel 'Watchit!'

**

Feline Friends

The dog sits quietly beside the cat pole, new, barely scratched. He watches Tabby reclining, slowly grooming himself in canine basket. Nearby the woman perches on the arm of the sofa, balancing her tea cup, watching Tortoiseshell stretching across several cushions. Humans did not foresee the use of the settee as a makeshift tree - with upholstery shredded, the hierarchy is embedded. Once the room empties, the two cats look up languidly, arch their backs and leave.

In the kitchen the smiling woman watches Tabby swishing his tail, stretching up at the cupboard, purr blink yawning, briefly fawning. Faced with the prospect of Gourmet Choice, his usual favourite, today Tabby elects to select a sniff, single lick with disdain; then goes into reverse gear to disappear. The human will clearly
need to think again, while Tabby reserves the right to abstain.

Tortoiseshell goes out awhile, amble-rambling then stopping for a lick, tail flick in the road. She fixes her stare on the driver, revving and fuming, so rude to intrude on her stroll. This feline does not care, has as long as it takes to wait, she is never early or late, until this stupid man becomes aware, this and any other day, that he is in the lady's way.

Tabby cogitates, contemplates throughout daylight hours, lounging long in the living room's single shade-spot, shifting slowly with the sliver. There is the merest hint of ear-flick as a fly, not worthy of an opened eye, alights, but cannot agitate this cat in the state of living in the present, his mind full of peace, attention focused on naught, emptying all thought.

Meanwhile, Tortoiseshell, back home and lying in shade, cleans her paws, yielding to a stretch. She watches the man, topless, boil toiling on his car, oven baked, sun stripped, then turns towards the tiles awhile, fur marble-cooled, to water bowl lick lap. Seeing the man suddenly gasp grasping on the gravel drive, just barely alive in the Spanish heat wave's dread forty-five, the cat strolls over, pads around the body, prone, and slinks under the car.

Email: richard@seal2244.fsnet.co.uk

Tel: (0034) 622 299 367

**

A man went to church one day and afterward he stopped to shake the preacher's hand.

He said, 'Preacher, I'll tell you, that was a damned fine sermon. Damned good!'

The preacher said, 'Thank you sir, but I'd rather you didn't use profanity.'

The man said, 'I was so damned impressed with that sermon I put five thousand dollars in the offering plate!'

The preacher said, 'No shit?'

An Accident at Sea

A true story. ***Percy & George were close friends in the nineteen sixties and seventies each owning a sea going yacht. George's boat was a Dufour 35, with all the equipment to sail safely, a long time after this story he eventually retired and sailed it to Ibiza. Percy's boat, although it had six berths and was quite happy at sea, the six cylinder diesel was a bit expensive to run, long journeys were not practical.***

On an occasion in November having a glass or two in a bar, George and I decided to sail to Oostende in Belgium, to get some sailing practice in. We studied the charts and the tides and we came to the conclusion it would be better to leave in the evening catching the falling water to help us on the way.

We took the craft out of the difficult entrance to the marina checking everything was in order. We knew what the compass bearings were. As it would be an overnight crossing we would take it in turns to navigate while the other rested. While George got his head down, so he could take the next watch, he issued me with navigation instructions and we were off, and I was to wake him at a certain point.

I do not know how boats find their way around today, probably by GPS, but then it was by compass and Admiralty sea charts.

I took the boat down the Blackwater and out to sea. George's instructions were to sail at a certain compass bearing and after about half an hour I would see a buoy with a flashing light and to aim for it. Each one flashes in a ten second sequence a serious of coded lights so it is possible at night to read this sequence to confirm your whereabouts.

Sure enough there it was. The night was pitch black, which made it difficult to judge distances. The waves in the water were not too rough and I sat in the cockpit with the tiller in my hand, keeping an eye on the compass and watching the light which was steadily coming towards us – I was mesmerised with its constant flashing. Suddenly it was just in front of the yacht its bright white light reflecting off the sails.

It was large, taller than the boat, the light flashing on and off in a certain coded pattern, to show its name as marked on the charts. We were sailing slightly into the wind, I quickly swung the rudder over hoping we would go round it, but I had turned the wrong way and it did not happen. We hit it just behind our starboard bow and the thing slid down the side of the boat in a bouncing movement with loud 'BANG, BANG, BANG' before it was behind us.

George came rushing up from below and shouted "I told you to aim for it not f******? hit it!"

The buoy had a very thick rubber type band around it which prevented any damage, we sailed on. It was a very frightening experience for both of us, sinking in the North Sea in November would not have been funny. Unfortunately the wind dropped and in the middle of the month and mid winter we became becalmed over the other side of the English Channel with not even a breeze to help us along, we had to return using the inboard diesel engine. There was not enough fuel to take us all the way back to Bradwell, but by taking the shorter crossing to Ramsgate was manageable.

Dorothy and Edna

Dorothy “I know you went out with Dennis last week, he has asked me out and I wanted to talk with you about him before I give him my answer."

Edna: "Well, I'll tell you. He shows up at my apartment punctually at 7 pm, dressed like such a gentleman in a fine suit, and he brings me such beautiful flowers! Then he takes me downstairs. And what's there; a limousine, uniformed chauffeur and all. Then he takes me out for dinner; a marvellous dinner, lobster, champagne, dessert, and after-dinner drinks. Then we go see a show. Let me tell you Dorothy, I enjoyed it so much I could have just died from pleasure!

So then we are coming back to my apartment and he turns into an ANIMAL. Completely crazy, he tears off my expensive new dress and has his way with me three times!"

Dorothy: "Goodness gracious!... so you are telling me I shouldn’t go near him?”

Edna: "No, no, no... I'm just saying, wear an old dress."

**

The Brains of Older People

By Sarah KNAPTON, Science Correspondent

Older people do not decline mentally with age, it just takes them longer to recall facts because they have much more information in their brains, and scientists believe they are slow because they know so much.

Much like a computer struggles as the hard drive gets filled up, so too do humans take longer to access information, it has been suggested.

Researchers say this slowing down it is not the same as cognitive decline.

"The human brain works slower in old age," said Dr. Michael RAMSCAR, "but only because we have stored more information over time. The brains of older people do not get weak. On the contrary, they simply know more."

Also, older people often go to another room to get something and when they get there, they stand there wondering what they came for. It is not a memory problem, it is nature's way of making older people get more exercise."

So there! We're all brilliant no matter how old!

**

The Vasectomy

After having their 11th child, a couple decided that was enough, as the social couldn't buy them a bigger bed and they weren't strong enough to nick one. The husband went to his doctor and told him that he and his wife didn't want to have any more children.

The doctor told him there was a procedure called a vasectomy that would fix the problem but it was expensive.

A less costly alternative was to go home, get a firework, light it, put it in a beer can, then hold the can up to his ear and count to 10. The man said to the doctor, "I may not be the smartest guy in the world, but I don't see how putting a firework in a beer can next to my ear is going to help me."

Trust me, it will do the job", said the doctor.

So the man went home, lit a banger and put it in a beer can. He held the can up to his ear and began to count: "1, 2, 3, 4, 5," at which point he paused, placed the beer can between his legs so he could continue counting on his other hand.

This procedure also works in Middlesbrough, parts of Bradford and anywhere in Wales also in the States.

**

Adam and Eve

When God created Adam and Eve, He said: I only have two gifts: One is the art of peeing standing ...And then Adam stepped forward and shouted:...ME!, ME!, ME!,I would love it please ... Lord, please, please! Look, it will make my life substantially easier. Eve nodded, and said those things did not matter to her. Then God gave Adam the gift and he began to shout for joy. He ran through the garden of Eden and used it to wet all the trees and bushes, ran down the beach making drawings with his pee in the sand ...Well, he would not stop showing off.

God and Eve watched the man crazy with happiness and Eve asked God: What is the other gift?

God answered: Eve,..... a brain ... and it is for you ...!

**

A Game of Golf

A husband and wife are on the 9th green when suddenly she collapses from a heart attack!

"Help me dear," she groans to her husband.

The husband calls 911 on his cell phone, talks for a few minutes, picks up his putter, and lines up his putt.

His wife raises her head off the green and stares at him.

"I'm dying here and you're putting?"

"Don't worry dear," says the husband calmly, "they found a doctor on the second hole and he's coming to help you.

"Well, how long will it take for him to get here?" she asks feebly.

"No time at all," says her husband. "Everybody's already agreed to let him play through."

A Pint of Guinness

Patrick walks into a bar in Dublin and orders three pints of Guinness and sits in the corner of the room. He takes a sip from each pint in turn. When he had finished all three He went back to the bar and ordered three more.

The barman says "You know the beer goes flat as soon as I pull it...why don't you buy one at a time and then it would taste better as it would be fresh?"

Patrick replies "Well now I have two brothers...one in America and the other in Australia and here is me in Dublin. When we all left home we promised we would always drink this way to remember the days when we used to drink together."

The barman admits that is a nice custom and says no more.

Patrick becomes a regular customer always drinking the same way – ordering three pints taking a sip from each until they are finished.

One day he comes into the bar and orders just two pints and goes over to the corner and sits down taking a sip from each. The regulars in the bar looked at each other and fell silent. When he returns to the bar for two more pints the barman says "I don't mean to intrude on your grief but I wanted to offer my condolences on your great loss."

Patrick looks confused for the moment, and then he realises what the barmen was indicating "Oh no," he says, "Bejesus, everyone is fine! Tis me,---I've quit Drinking !"

**

Heart Surgery

An Arab Sheik was admitted to Hospital for heart surgery, but prior to the surgery, the doctors needed to have some of his blood type stored, in case the need arose.

As the gentleman had a rare type of blood, it couldn't be found locally, so, the call went out. Finally a Scotsman was located who had the same rare blood type. The Scot willingly donated his blood for the Arab.

After the surgery, the Arab sent the Scotsman, as appreciation for giving his blood, a new BMW, a diamond necklace for his wife, and $100,000 US dollars.

A couple of days later, the Arab had to go through a corrective surgery procedure. Once again, his doctor telephoned the Scotsman who was more than happy to donate his blood.

After the second surgery, the Arab sent the Scotsman a thank-you card and a box of Quality Street chocolates. The Scotsman was shocked that the Arab did not reciprocate his kind gesture as he had anticipated.

He phoned the Arab and asked him: "I thought you would be generous again, that you would give me another BMW, diamonds and money, but you only gave me a thank-you card and a box of Quality Street chocolates."

To this the Arab replied: "Aye laddie, but I now have Scottish blood in me veins".

**

What a wonderful world!

"May Your God grant you always...

A sunbeam to warm you,

a moonbeam to charm you,

a sheltering Angel so nothing can harm you,

Laughter to cheer you.

Faithful friends near you.

And whenever you pray, God to hear you."

-- An Irish Blessing

**

My get up and go
got up and went.
If you see it, would you
remind it that it left me.

Thanks and that's all for now see you next time

Time
Gentlemen
PERCY W. CHATTEY
POLITICALLY
INCORRECT
The thrilling story of an
assassination plot and a romantic web
of betrayal that threatens the
very heart of the government and
the heart of a family,
... is it all worth it?
PERCY W. CHATTEY

THE
BLACK VENUS
A Story of Love,
Murder & Revenge
PERCY W. CHATTEY
BLITZ & PIECES
THE TRUE STORY OF HOW A
SIX YEAR OLD SURVIVED
THE LONDON BLITZ
An Autobiography
PERCY W. CHATTEY

DEATH FOR
A STARTER
The Murderous Story
of the O'Dowd family
PERCY W. CHATTEY

WATCHit!
there's love about
PERCY W. CHATTEY
Treble Pinnacle Book Award Winner THRILLER WRITER
WATCHIT - THERE'S LOVE ABOUT
PERCY W. CHATTEY

WATCH it too!
THRILLER WRITER
PERCY W. CHATTEY
Mutliple Pinnacle Book Award Winner
The Dauntless Factor
Pinnacle Book Achievement Award
PERCY W. CHATTEY

Made in the USA
Columbia, SC
22 May 2017